D0876481

DATE DUE

The Silken Angels

AIRMEN & AIRCRAFT
Martin Caidin, General Editor

Also:

HERITAGE OF VALOR, by Colonel Budd J. Peaslee, USAF Retired

TRACKS ACROSS THE SKY, by Page Shamburger

THE
SILKEN
ANGELS

A History of Parachuting

By Martin Caidin

J. B. LIPPINCOTT COMPANY
PHILADELPHIA AND NEW YORK
1964

629.13

THIS BOOK IS FOR

JOSEPH W. KITTINGER, JR.
Captain, United States Air Force

A CLOSE FRIEND, AN OUTSTANDING
TEST PILOT, AND A MAN DEDICATED
TO MAKING THE SKIES SAFER FOR
OTHER MEN WHO FLY

Contents

The Silken Angels

CHAPTER 1

An Angel for Every Pilot

SIXTEEN THOUSAND FEET above the earth a small airplane slides along a great sloping wall of clouds. The sky is a rich blue, the white clouds lofty and towering. It is one of those rare and wonderful days when there are just enough clouds to create massive white mountains and shadowed valleys through which an airplane can dart and soar.

It is a day that pilots say is made just for flying, when a pilot on the ground feels his feet begin to itch and his fingers bend searchingly for a stick and a throttle knob. The earth seems leaden and heavy, as though a great chain weighed upon everyone, and the skies call beseechingly to any man who has ever known the wonder of feeling a powerful machine respond instantly to a flick of his wrist.

Far above the earth, one young man has answered the call. Moving with all the grace and agility of a hummingbird, his plane is so tiny against those massive ramparts of cloud that from the ground it seems no larger than the merest speck. The plane whirls and falls; it leaps and then sails gently along the currents streaming from cloud to cloud. It is an airplane built by hand, its fuselage silver and the wings a gaudy pattern of orange and white stripes.

The pilot is up there for the pure joy of flight. He does not carry out his maneuvers with particular and grim precision. Instead, he floats and wafts through the cloud gorges, along the tumbled slopes; he moves through brilliant sun, standing the little biplane on its wingtips to ease through narrow canyons; he follows the cloud ridges and pursues the gaps in the walls. It is hard to believe that these are clouds and not walls of solid granite. It is heady and exhilarating to fly this way; the wind sings past the open cockpit of the biplane, and the pilot senses its shifts and changes as his speed rises and falls in response to his maneuvers.

And then what is beautiful becomes breathtaking. Along the edge of a great mass so towering that it soars completely out of sight, the clouds tumble and fall in prominences and gorges. There are walls and cliffs and ravines of clouds. Along the edges small puffballs are broken away by the winds; as the biplane dashes through the flimsy mists, a hand seems to slap it gently. The pilot feels this touch of wind and laughs aloud with the sensations of the flying.

In the distance the wall is black; but it *is* in the distance and so the biplane's pilot ignores the warning signs that are building rapidly all about him. The ground no longer is as visible as before: streaks of clouds have slid in between the little airplane and the green earth. The sunlight is no longer as brilliant as before. Great shadows spear the cloud formations, signifying the rapid building and flowering of cloud petals much higher than the man in his small machine.

The air no longer is gentle in its touches of turbulence: there are slaps of wind more severe than before. Now, when a wing goes down, the pilot must exert greater pressure with the stick and his rudder to bring it back to level flight.

For several minutes the young man senses these things, but they fail to register the warnings that they convey to the more experienced pilot. The clouds are rearing steeply, more so than before, and they are bulging with energy. The mass of clouds which were so pleasant to fly through have bulled and pushed and shouldered their mass into a wall of thunderstorms growing with astonishing speed.

The pilot sees a long canyon ahead of him. It is enough; he will slide down the tremendous ravine toward the earth and come down below the clouds. Then, knowing the countryside as well as his own hand, he will establish his position and race for his home airfield at low altitude . . . to end an absolutely perfect day in the heavens.

He pulls on a knob; warm air floods the carburetor system, so that when he drops through the clouds, with his engine reduced in power, ice will not form in the carburetor throat. (More than one pilot has lost his engine that way!)

He slides the throttle control back toward him. The roar of the engine ebbs and becomes a throaty hum; the propeller spins less rapidly. In smoothly coordinated movement, the pilot eases the stick forward and slightly to the left, simultaneously applying pressure with his left foot to the rudder pedal. The airplane rolls into a wide curving spiral and drops her nose, sailing around in a long and controlled turn toward the earth.

The biplane rounds a corner of the cloud canyon—and the pilot feels his heart leap into his throat. *For there is no way out.* His exhilaration of flight has subdued his common sense and blinded him to the storm warnings through which he has flown. He is in a box canyon.

Panic becomes a live passenger in the cockpit with him as he eases the throttle forward. Below him the earth is gone, vanished beneath the ugly gray scud whipping rapidly over the surface. The fear rises as he realizes he is boxed in at the edge of a mighty thunderhead, a giant cumulo-nimbus cloud, a dreaded giant armed with howling winds and forked spears of lightning.

Engine pounding with the sudden power, the airplane claws around in a tight turn. The pilot must get out—and get out now—or the energy raging within those cloud walls will engulf him.

But there is no way out. All about him the clouds have closed in, an overwhelming mass. In bare minutes the complexion of the entire world has changed. The sun no longer is visible; blue sky is replaced with leaden gray. There is no way to   ody of the pilot. By now he is t   should have been many, many n

He i‹   s the little airplane in its tight tu   the air heaves and rocks the pla   ere loading on the wings. And th   ⁊ of the pilot is stripped from hi   ⊃less pawn.

He ‹   ith electricity. A bolt of lightnii   side of one canyon wall and punctures the opposite wall of cloud. The light is impossibly bright; instinctively, the pilot throws his arm before his eyes. He is completely unprepared for the thunderclap that follows, a deafening blast of sound that smites his ears with a physical blow. In just those seconds, as he reacts to the lightning and the roar of thunder, the biplane slides into the wall of cloud. In the time-honored expression of thousands of pilots, all hell breaks loose.

Inside these thunderstorms are winds that shriek and howl like demons. They plunge straight down at more than a hundred miles per hour, sometimes twice as fast. Only feet away another blast of air may howl straight up. Between the two of them, they exert an unbelievable shearing effect; they can grasp an airplane as though it were a fragile, lacy toy and in a twinkling tear it into shreds.

Not too long ago, two pilots in a powerful Canberra jet bomber entered a true giant of a thundercloud. They flew into the cloud at 14,000 feet, and, in their own words, "The world went stark, raving mad." The storm ripped control of their machine from their hands. In seconds, it inundated the jet engines with torrents of water and flamed them out. Hail smashed the nose and the leading edges of the wings and cracked their curving Plexiglas canopy into jagged shards. They were flung about madly—and when they could once again see, their fear was so great they could not speak.

That storm hurled their heavy bomber straight up for nearly ten miles! The giant cumulo-nimbus cloud spit them from its innards in a disdainful stroke of good fortune at more than 60,000 feet. The airplane came out of the storm upside down, without power, looking as though it had been mauled for an hour by a battering ram. The pressure cabin gaped open, and only the pressure suits that squeezed the bodies of the men kept them alive. Miraculously, they regained control at about 25,000 feet and managed to bring their airplane in—deadstick —at an emergency field.

This storm is not nearly so tall or wide or powerful, but it *is* a thunderstorm, and it has full control of the little biplane. The pilot is completely helpless as the airplane whirls crazily, a dervish gone mad. He has absolutely no control; indeed, the control stick responds to the fluttering of the ailerons and lashes back and forth wildly in the narrow cockpit. The stick pummels the pilot's knees and thighs, and he cries out in pain. He can feel water stinging into his face and drenching his clothes, but everything is blurred. He knows he is gyrating helplessly through the cloud, but there is nothing he can do. The forces of the wild careening pin him helplessly within the airplane.

And then there is a great, tearing *crack!* The pilot watches in horror as the wing spar folds like a matchstick snapped in two and the wing flashes away in the storm. The blackness is punctuated with jagged and searing bolts of light. Terrified, he does not even realize for several seconds that the storm has spit him clear: he is in a mass of wreckage only 2000 feet above the ground, tumbling earthward, while the rest of the airplane disintegrates about him.

Later, he cannot recall his actions exactly. He remembers freeing his seat belt and clawing his way from the whirling cockpit. He cannot break free, and he has a dim memory of shoving with all his might against the torn fabric of the biplane. There is a moment, the first in many, when no longer is there any pounding or roaring. Only then does he realize that his body is falling through space, that he is clear of the wreckage, that instinctively and automatically he has rejected his broken airplane—and placed his hope of survival entirely on the operation of a pack strapped by a harness to his falling body.

He remembers a long moment of peace and a feeling of wonder and pleasantness. With a rude shock, he becomes aware of the earth moving up to meet him. He shakes off the feeling of peace. His right hand grasps a metal ring and yanks hard. He pulls with such force that his outstretched hand flings away the metal ring and a piece of steel cable attached to it.

But it no longer matters. The young pilot is only 800 feet above the earth when a long streamer of nylon spills from the pack strapped to his body. There is a sudden, hard jolt.

The pilot looks up and his face creases in a wide, joyful grin. Above his head floats a mass of white—billowing folds of nylon that, attached to shroud lines leading to the harness about his body, lower him gently to earth.

The parachute rocks slightly in the wind currents from the storm that nearly snuffed out his life. But such movements are a delight. Only moments ago the young man was about to die; he had blundered into the maw of a storm that ripped his machine to pieces. Now, from the very jaws of death, he drifts gently toward the green earth. With a speed just above ten miles per hour he sails toward the ground, drifting over the surface with the wind. He is lucky; the parachute will drop him in an open field.

He has no experience at this sort of thing. He strikes the ground with a heavy thump that drives the air from his lungs. Clumsily, he falls to the ground, wrenching his shoulder. Gritting his teeth, he clambers to his feet to spill the air still in the canopy and prevent his being dragged before the breeze. Then, finally, he stands, unhooking the harness. His shoulder aches, and he is slightly bruised and scratched. A cheap price to pay for life itself!

He looks up at the sky, at the black wall looming into the heavens. He sees the tongues of lightning spearing crazily through the air, hears the deep rolls of thunder. With a sense of awe he realizes that *that* is what he has just escaped. He is very grateful. Carefully he gathers his parachute, bundles it together, and starts to walk toward a farmhouse in the distance.

When he gets home, he is going to clean and repack that parachute. Then he is going to hang it neatly on the wall of his room. And he knows that he will look at that chute, often, and think of it as the silken angel that gave him back his life. . . .

This is our story—the silken angels. Not one, of course, and certainly not all. But a history of the angels that have lowered men to earth through the course of many years of flying: in peacetime, in war, in moments of peril, and in moments totally unexpected and shockingly sudden.

The sky is high, impossibly wide and unbelievably big; it is not really a sky, it is an ocean—an ocean of air that at rare moments is still and serene. Most of the time the ocean is filled with invisible rocks and reefs: winds that surge and spill, tumbling over and over, sometimes with devastating force; dust and water vapor; all manner of gases; lightning, and the crackling roar of thunderbolts. It is filled with clouds, and ghostly light, and bright clean sunshine.

But the sky is also penetrated, and at any time of day or night in some part of the world there are hundreds of airplanes aloft. Sometimes, men fight wars, exerting their every effort to smash and destroy the airplanes of others. It seems a shame that something so beautiful and filled with grace as an airplane should be employed in such a manner—but it is also a fact of life.

The air is solid—to a wing. The shape of a wing and its movement through the gaseous ocean we call air generates controlled forces about that wing. It produces lift, and machines that weigh many thousands of pounds are made to do wonderful things high above the earth.

The air is solid to a wing, but much less so to a human body; without the support of the wing (and the entire airplane), the human body will fall. It isn't the fall, one man said, but that last half inch that hurts so much. The rest of it is easy.

To take the punch out of that last half inch, some men devised the parachute. In essence, it is a great canopy, once of silk and now almost always of nylon and other miracle fabrics. Nylon shroud lines run from the rim of the canopy to a harness, and if a man is strapped securely within that harness—why, he can do all sorts of impossible things, defy the odds and death itself, and survive.

We cannot know exactly how many men have lived who otherwise would have died, were it not for the silken angels they strapped to their bodies, but, since the first men with foresight developed a parachute that could be produced and distributed in large numbers, well over one hundred thousand men have survived what otherwise would have been certain death. Some of their stories are incredible; others border on the impossible. But all of them are true.

We are not talking about parachute jumps made for sport,

or exhibitions, or testing (although this too is a part of our story), or of men who jump in large numbers, as paratroopers. Those men perform their actions under control and quite deliberately. Our story is of those men who jumped for their lives—because if they did not they would die.

It is a wonderful story, in many ways. It tells us in dramatic and moving terms of the ability of the human being to endure, and to overcome, impossible odds. Thus our story is not only of the silken angels—but also of the men who were borne beneath them to safety.

CHAPTER 2

Circus in the Sky

ONE OF THE FIRST parachute jumps took place in the year 1785. The parachutist did not want to jump. He opposed the idea so violently that he was picked up by the scruff of the neck and heaved bodily over the side of a balloon drifting high over France.

The passenger who made this early descent by parachute even tried to bite the man who sent him on his way, which is understandable, since the parachutist was an unfortunate—and snarling—stray mongrel seized on the streets of Paris by Jean Pierre Blanchard, an enterprising French balloonist.

Lest we think too harshly of M. Blanchard, it must be noted that eight years later he also went over the side of his balloon basket and descended by parachute to the earth. The dog, being lighter than the Frenchman, had landed unharmed. The Frenchman did not. Upon striking the ground M. Blanchard fractured a leg, but the pain seems to have been worth the results. For the next several years, Blanchard was the most famous man in Europe.

His fame soon was to be eclipsed. Blanchard made one

jump, and that was all; his reluctance to leap again from a balloon may be ascribed to the pain of his broken leg and the conviction that "once is enough; twice may be the end of it."

In 1797, the first true parachutist captured the attention of all Europe. On October 22 of that year, André Jacques Garnerin clambered into a small basket suspended beneath a balloon drifting 2000 feet above Paris. Heavy cords attached the balloon to a folded mass of linen. Secure in the basket, Garnerin cut himself free and plummeted toward the city. The linen caught the wind, spread out with a healthy *whoomp!*, and the Frenchman began his moment of history.

On the way down, Garnerin feared that success might not be his. The parachute he employed was at best a clumsy and crude device. No one then understood the principles of stabilizing the parachute, and the entire affair oscillated so violently from side to side that the Frenchman hung on for his very life. The basket swung so wildly that, more than once, Garnerin actually was lifted to a position higher than that of his canopy. His clutching hands, however, proved adequate to the task, and he stepped from the basket to receive the roaring ovation of a quickly assembling crowd.

During the next several years, Garnerin continued to jump throughout France, and in England as well. His leaps into space while he clung grimly to his fragile basket made him an international figure. Undoubtedly he owed his continued success and survival to the work of a contemporary, the French astronomer Lalande, who solved the problem of stopping the wilder oscillations of the descending parachute-basket system.

Other men began to jump from balloons, but their names are lost to history. Not all survived. The fabric parachutes often were assembled by amateurs—and everyone was at that time an amateur—and they failed to withstand the forces of dropping from the sky. Some daring men lacked the grip that Garnerin made famous, and they tumbled from their baskets.

Others never had the opportunity to test their parachutes, since their balloons collapsed during flight and carried the whole assembly crashing to the earth.

As the years passed, men continued to work on the problem of improved stabilization in the parachutes with which they hoped to jump. Robert Cocking, an English inventor, disdained the work of others to perfect his own parachute design. On the evening of July 24, 1837, Cocking searched the area of Vauxhall Gardens in London for—of all things—a stray dog. Lacking Blanchard's success, he quickly stepped into his balloon basket, ordered the lines freed, and sailed off into the sky.

The Englishman soared to 5000 feet over the city, took a deep breath and a strong grip on his contraption, and cut himself free. For a moment, perhaps several, Cocking dropped smoothly and under control. And then, as many predicted, the strain proved excessive: the framework of Cocking's invention snapped like a rifle shot, and he plunged to his death.

There were many tests made with crude parachutes. The less courageous—or less affluent—inventors climbed to the tops of towers. Here they hurled their bodies into the air in the hope that their parachutes would open and lower them safely to the ground. History has paid scant attention to the uncounted number of broken limbs and backs, of sprains and bruises, or even to those unfortunates who ended their brief journey with a sickening thud into the ground. The wiser of these experimenters usually piled hay into high mounds beneath the towers—just in case.

Cocking's death, because of the great attention accorded it by London newspapers, had implications far out of proportion to the importance of his jump. His parachute was from the beginning ill-conceived; nevertheless, the feeling spread quickly that parachutes might be fun for daring roustabouts at circuses and fairs but were useless as lifesaving devices. Among the men and even the women who sailed the skies in gaily colored balloons, the parachute came to be regarded as vulgar. To carry one was to deny one's faith in the balloon. In addition, the association of parachutes with circus and fair performers was considered a taint, and balloonists sneered at anyone who jumped.

Fortunately for the entertainment of the thousands of people who flocked to the fairs held throughout England and France, the "vulgar" parachutists far outnumbered the bluenoses who sailed as a clique. There was money to be made in falling through the sky before large crowds, and daredevils plus money add up to men who will try anything.

Some of these men became quite skilled in their jumping. Actually, the term *jumping* is a misnomer. The balloons used in those days for circus acts had a hanging bar suspended beneath the large bag of the balloon proper. The parachutist would clamber onto this bar before ascent, clinging to it as would a monkey. High over the earth, he would reach up and open the gas-release valve of the balloon, and then release his grip.

As he fell away from the balloon, his body encased in a harness, a light cord tied to his body would snap from the weight of his fall. This cord released the folded parachute, which would stream after the jumper and, within a second or two, pop open in the wind; the man would drift to the earth, waving to the crowd.

The real action began as he hit the ground. Now the jumper had to move fast. He would leap into a waiting horse and buggy—or sometimes just atop a horse—and go pellmell across the countryside to retrieve his descending balloon. This was done amid shrieking voices and barking dogs, for an army of children and frenzied animals rushed after their hero. With the balloon safely in his hands, the "death-defying aeronaut" trudged back to the fairgrounds to demand his fee.

Such fees were invariably paid after a successful jump, not

before. The men who ran the fairs and hired the jumpers saw little reason to pay the fee beforehand; the odds were high that the jumper would come down with the parachute streaming or collapsed. After striking the ground in this fashion, a jumper never got to his feet in pursuit of money; he never regained his feet at all. For the fair owner this proved to be wonderful business. The crowd enjoyed the thrill and excitement of watching a man plunge to his death, and it cost the owner nothing. Naturally, the next aeronaut would draw an even bigger crowd, on the chance that the same incident might be repeated.

It is easy to understand why the parachute, except for these open-air theatrical performances, remained for many years in disfavor. To be sure, some men saved their lives with parachutes, but there were only a few such cases. In these incidents, the men involved were aerial circus performers whose balloons failed them on their way aloft; fortunately, they were all set to leap from their trapeze bars under any circumstances.

At the same time, it seems strange that greater effort was not applied to develop workable lifesaving parachutes. Balloons were ideal vehicles from which to jump. When a balloon drifts through the skies, it is in a state of perfect balance, which is why it maintains a continuous altitude. If the amount of lifting gas is reduced, the balloon descends. But if the weight carried by the balloon is decreased—by the dropping of ballast, for example—the balloon gains buoyancy and immediately rises.

This is a most important factor in jumping. A man who leaps from a drifting balloon knows that he will not become entangled in the basket suspended beneath the balloon. As he drops away from the balloon, his aerial vehicle immediately becomes lighter, lifts higher into the sky, and thus moves in a direction opposite to that of the jumper.

Notwithstanding these facts, the parachute remained sus-

Airplanes weren't necessary for testing parachutes in the early days of aviation. A gangplank off the Kings Bridge in England served this daredevil well, and he was successfully fished from the river below. (Air Force)

pect, and most balloonists continued to take unnecessary chances.

The airplane changed the picture completely.

For many years after the Wright Brothers ushered in the era of powered and controlled aircraft flight in December, 1903, parachutes were never used in flying. But there was a growing list of casualties. Most people who flew in the early days were heroes to the public. Flying itself was a daring and dangerous occupation, and the men who took to the skies on wings were a daring breed. Soon they began to challenge one another to see who could fly the fastest, or the highest, or make the sharpest turns. These competitions usually brought out great crowds of people, and roars of dismay went up when favorite heroes were injured or killed before their very eyes.

Balloons were much safer than airplanes in the early days of flying. A balloon lifted gently, and in flight it drifted with the wind. Unless the wind blew so hard that the balloon was dashed against the ground in landing, the flights proved safe. Movement was calm. Directional control proved impossible, but a descent could be initiated at any time simply by releasing the lifting gas.

The airplane proved much more dangerous. First, no airplane could gain lift, and flight, from its wings unless it moved at a certain speed. The very nature of its flight demanded speed—and speed in those days seemed to mean accidents.

It is difficult today, when we see supersonic fighters and great jet airliners, to remember just how flimsy those old machines really were. Made of wood or light metal tubing, covered with fabric or canvas, many of them barely remained in one piece while flying in calm air. And when the air became turbulent . . .

Pilots knew very little of the movement of air. The atmos-

"Widely used" in the period 1910-1917, the Wright Model B was fragile, underpowered, unbalanced—and dangerous. (Air Force)

phere could be felt, because of wind, and sometimes dust and water vapor, or haze, could be seen. But the currents and movements, and especially the forces, of the air were a complete mystery. Men took off in their small airplanes. Hundreds of feet above the ground they encountered turbulent air currents that were completely invisible. These sudden gusts often tipped the machines to dangerous angles or snapped wings completely off. Some of the airplanes remained in one piece but were flung out of control, falling to the ground.

In the year 1910, the number of airplane deaths caused a public outcry. Both men and women were flying, and the casualties began to grow: Delagrange, Rolls, Johnstone, Lefebvre, Moisant, Hoxsey—these well-known figures and thirty-one others died, and dozens more were badly injured or crippled that year.

The onlookers on the ground were unable to help their friends because neither they, nor the other pilots, really understood why many of the accidents happened. The weak structures crumpled in mid-air. The fabric clung weakly to frames and tore loose in the wind. Flapping crazily, it stripped the wings—and the machine plummeted.

As the *Scientific American* sadly noted, in 1910, "Usually no one knows what happened in the air. A mangled body is taken

Some pilots flew to the brink of death—and stopped short. In this extraordinary crash, the pilot didn't receive a scratch. (Air Force)

from a mass of wreckage, and we can only guess what caused the accident."

Not always, because sometimes the simplest things caused an accident—and a death. The early pilots lacked even the crudest of safety devices. Airplanes took off and performed maneuvers without a safety belt—or even a rope!—to secure the pilot to his machine. Aviators sat on wood slats; they were exposed to the wind. One accident took place when a large insect flew with stinging force against the eye of a pilot; he lifted his hands to his eye as a reaction to the pain, and the machine fell off and spun into the ground.

Airplanes at times react violently to turbulence. If the airplane is not inherently stable—and those ancient ships were not—even a slight gust of wind can tip the machine on its side or drop the nose sharply. In turbulence the pilots did not know whether to fly their airplanes or simply hang on for dear life, to keep from being tossed out. It is impossible to do both at the same time. The result was inevitable: more people died. Some were pitched away from their airplanes to fall to their death.

The great tragedy of all this we can recognize today. Had these people had no more than the crudest of safety belts and parachutes, many of them would have lived.

Certain improvements began to appear in airplanes. Enclosed cockpits shielding pilot and passengers reduced the impact of the wind. First ropes, and then special belts, were added for pilot safety. Engineers built greater strength into their planes, so that a minor landing mishap did not become a disaster. Airplanes became more stable and were not so likely to tumble out of control because of a strong gust of wind.

But the parachute, the one device that could have saved dozens of lives, remained absent. Ironically, pilots did not clamor for parachutes; in fact, they shunned them like the plague.

It is not difficult to understand why they ridiculed the idea of using parachutes to save their lives—even men who sought a means of improving their chances of survival finally agreed that the parachute could not help them—when we read about the first jump ever made from an airplane.

This epochal event took place on a calm day in March, 1912, at Jefferson Barracks, Missouri. Captain Bert Berry of the Army planned to make the world's first jump from an airplane. The airplane from which Berry planned to jump was a rickety machine known as the *Benoist Pusher*, flown by his close friend, Tony Jannus. Many of Berry's friends, learning of his decision, tried to dissuade the captain from "certain suicide."

Berry did not wear his parachute, as chutes in those days did not fit into packs. The men packed the device into a metal cone which they bolted to the forward part of the belly of the airplane. In order to prepare to jump, Berry had to climb down from his seat, straddle the axle of the *Benoist*, and then —in the wind and rocking motion of the airplane—slip into the harness!

This alone was enough to convince the average pilot that Berry would never survive. It was hard enough to perform such a feat, but to do so and then climb into the harness was considered almost impossible.

Berry was undaunted. His clothes whipped flat against his body by the wind, he slipped down onto the axle and wriggled into the harness. Then he fell away backward, clearing the landing gear, and tumbled into space. The weight of his falling body hauled the parachute from its metal container, snapped a retaining cord, and exposed the canopy to the wind. Despite the unfavorable odds, Berry performed the jump in complete safety.

Recognizing the amazing agility required to make this sort of jump, it is obvious that the parachute so used had no value as a lifesaving device. The technique required that the pilot keep the airplane flying straight and level. Conditions of flight also were required to be smooth.

Diminutive "Tiny" Broadwick was famous around the world as a daring parachutist who made hundreds of leaps from balloons and planes. This is Tiny as she appeared just before the world's first jump from a "hydro-aeroplane," piloted by Glenn L. Martin, on August 17, 1913. Note the balloon-type parachute. (Jim Greenwood Archives)

If the air were turbulent, the business of climbing down to the airplane's axle, slipping into the harness, and jumping would be impossible. In an emergency situation in the air, the airplane may be on fire or have suffered structural damage or breakup. In any case, the machine would be falling out of control and possibly disintegrating as it fell. No man could then go through the laborious process followed by Captain Berry.

The parachute, therefore, was felt to be an interesting device, but good for little else. It provided splendid entertainment at fairs and circuses, and that was about all.

Then World War I began, and men took to the skies in accelerating numbers. As the war continued, the casualty list of pilots and airmen who died in combat soared into the hundreds, and then into the thousands. Finally, men came to realize that many of these deaths were completely unnecessary. The parachute, developed to be used as an emergency device, could have saved many men who lost their lives.

CHAPTER 3

A Choice of Dying

IN THE EARLY DAYS of World War I, pilots and their crew members were among the more fortunate of the men engaged in war. Their fragile machines clattered and sputtered to and fro, over the front trenches and sometimes on longer excursions behind enemy lines. As more airplanes took to the skies, encounters between these machines became commonplace. Enemies on the ground, the pilots observed a strange comradeship in the heavens; often, Ally and German waved in greeting to one another as the airplanes passed, each on its mission of carrying messages or supplies or of observing the activities of enemy forces on the ground.

This state of affairs, lauded by most of the men who winged their way over the front, did not last too long. There was a war underway. The purpose of fighting wars is to achieve victory. In warfare, this has always involved killing the enemy.

The early airplanes were ludicrous as weapons. Their wings and fuselages were flimsy, sometimes consisting of bare framework stretching from a small gondola back to the tail. They reeked of gasoline and oil, their engines were notoriously unreliable, and they were alarmingly fragile in their structure.

Every so often the engine would explode, or the airplane begin to burn, owing to nothing more than poor workmanship and shoddy materials.

One famous fighter was the Nieuport—as famous for shedding its wings in flight as it was for the many aces (like Rickenbacker) who flew this type of airplane. The Nieuport 11, an early model in the series, was powered with an 80 horsepower Le Rhone engine. Its wingspan was 29 feet 7 inches, and its length 18 feet 8 inches. Like other World War I fighters, the Nieuport 11 was a flyweight. Empty, it weighed only 774 pounds. Fully loaded with pilot, fuel, guns, and ammunition, it had a top speed of 97 miles per hour. The small fighter required twelve minutes to climb to a height of only 6500 feet.

Engineers rapidly overcame the worst of these difficulties. More powerful engines added speed to the airplanes; better design gave them greater strength. They could carry heavier loads into the sky than before. Add the development of improved machines to the imagination of fighting men, and war in the air was the inevitable result.

It was not aerial combat as we know it; those first fights would evoke roars of laughter among pilots today. A man would fly over an enemy airplane. According to custom, the enemy crew waved their greetings. But the man in the higher airplane did not wave back; instead, he heaved rocks and bricks at his acquaintance below. Sometimes the bricks cracked a skull or two, slammed into an engine, or tore holes in wings.

Inevitably, the man suffering from a severe bump on his head fought back. Finally, one observer stood up in a rear cockpit and blazed away with a pistol at a nearby airplane. The other observer, in turn, stood up and emptied the magazine of a rifle into the opposing airplane. One thing led to another, and from bricks and pistols the aircrews soon lugged machine guns into their machines. The next development came in the form of incendiary bullets, a terrifying weapon against

The Nieuport was agile as a dervish but tragically inflammable, and so weak in structure that in a dive the wings would shed their fabric and sometimes buckle completely. Parachutes would have saved the lives of many pilots who flew these and other fighters of World War I. (The National Archives)

the highly inflammable airplanes of World War I times; the fabric burned easily, fuel tanks were unprotected, and the dope (or glue) used to keep the fabric on the wings and body was explosively inflammable.

In no time at all, science and technology triumphed—a full-scale war in the air blazed over the trenches.

The people who regarded these events with the greatest apprehension were the observers manning the baskets of observation balloons just behind the front lines. The sausage-shaped balloons, filled with hydrogen gas, lifted from the ground on trailing cables. Sent to heights of several hundred to several thousand feet, they provided an excellent opportunity for an observer with binoculars, and even a telescope, to survey enemy activities, direct artillery fire, and generally prove a painful thorn in the side of the enemy.

During the first months of the war, the job of observer remained quite pleasant. It was quiet in the sky, the job was easy, and no one bothered to shoot at the balloons.

But then someone threw bricks, somebody else fired both barrels of a shotgun, and machine guns appeared on the scene. Very quickly the sausages drifting idly at the end of their slim cables became choice targets for sharpshooting pilots and gunners.

Naturally, this led the balloon observers to take frantic measures to save their lives, as what had been a coveted position became one of the most hated jobs in the war.

The hydrogen that filled the swollen balloons was incredibly dangerous. A single spark turned a balloon into a howling mass of fire that descended quickly upon the hapless observer in the basket. The heat of the flames, even from many feet away, could ignite an observer's clothing. They died in horrible fashion, either burning alive or, to save themselves this agony, by throwing their bodies over the sides of their baskets and plummeting to death.

Very quickly the observers began to modify their baskets. People had been parachute-jumping for years from free-drifting balloons—now the observers scurried to obtain parachutes for themselves. And they worked—not always, but often enough to save many lives.

The balloon observers slipped into the harness before leaving the ground. They secured the top of the parachute with a cord to the basket. Then, wearing the harness attached to the other end of the chute, the observer signaled to the ground crew to release the balloon for its ascent.

It was not long before the observers found the strain of wearing a parachute too much to endure for long hours in the baskets. As they began to improvise, the parachute began a new era of development—slow at first, but nonetheless meaningful. Desperation led to progress.

The observer slipped the shroud lines of the parachute into

"Tiny" Broadwick wearing her father's Safety
Pack, which she demonstrated to the U.S.
Army Signal Corps at San Diego, California,
in 1914. After the demonstration, the Army
bought the chute for further evaluations.
(Tiny Broadwick, who jumped from a
balloon at fifteen years of age, on June 21,
1913, became the world's first woman to jump
from an airplane.) (Jim Greenwood Archives)

a metal ring and then fastened lines and ring securely as a single unit. Wearing his harness all the time, all the observer needed to do to hook up his parachute was to snap the ring onto a hook of his harness and jump for his life.

The advantages of physical comfort sometimes proved fatal. The system of wearing the parachute continuously in the balloon basket may have been wearying, but at least the man knew—as he jumped frantically from the basket—that he had it on. Sometimes an observer had only split seconds in which to save his life. The balloons burned fiercely, mushrooming within seconds into great masses of flame. Unless the observer beat a hasty retreat at once, he knew that pieces of the blazing balloon, or even long tongues of flame, would reach his parachute, and he would fall to earth trailing not a lifesaving canopy but a streak of fire.

The need to get out and get out instantly turned many of the observers into nervous wrecks. Sometimes, at no more than the sound of an engine or the chatter of machine guns in the distance, they would fling themselves over the side of their basket. Even when an airplane drifted into view and did not fire, the observer was wont to dive for the earth. So quickly and explosively did the balloons go up in flames, it just did not pay to take any chances.

During these moments of panic, the price for comfort was sometimes death. Some observers looked up to see a wall of flames hurtling down upon them. Terrorized by the sight and by the heat playing on their bodies, they simply hurled themselves into the air, sometimes forgetting to hook the parachute ring to their harness first.

Whatever the problems, there no longer was any question of the tremendous value of the parachute in saving lives. No one, to say the least, could argue the point with the balloon observers, many of whom had jumped—not once but several times—to escape a blazing death.

The Broadwick Safety Pack of 1914 is worn here by Floyd Smith. To operate, the pilot attached a snubbing or static ripcord to the airplane and then bailed out. After a short fall, the pack cover would rip open, pulling out the canopy. (Air Force)

Improvements in the design of the parachutes came rapidly. German observers held in high esteem a woman stunt jumper, Kaethe Paulus, who devoted her energies to producing better parachutes for German personnel. The British and French, deciding not to leave the parachutes hanging limply outside the balloon baskets, packed them neatly into long conical containers, from which they pulled easily.

The next step, parachutes for the pilots and crewmen of airplanes, seemed inevitable. And designers went rapidly to work to meet this problem. Yet their efforts were not good enough, and for their energies they received the disdain and scorn of pilots.

Flying their brightly colored fighters, the pilots soon built up the legend that using a parachute was worse than not having one along. The men took their chances in battle—and rejected the parachute.

Today, we tend to look back upon the aerial combat of World War I and ascribe the attitude of the fighter pilots to the gallantry of their profession. Many writers have tried to prove that these pilots lived by tradition, and that wearing a parachute for lifesaving purposes would mean they no longer had confidence in themselves.

All of this is so much rubbish. There is nothing gallant or traditional about burning to death. The concept of being roasted alive appealed to no one, and any writer who claims that this danger was willingly accepted, when a good parachute would have prevented it, is an idiot.

When airplanes burned, many pilots knew they had a choice of dying. They could remain with their machines and be burned slowly to death or they could throw themselves away from their airplanes and fall to the quicker death that came with the impact of their bodies against the earth. Many men preferred the latter.

In May, 1918, one of the greatest and best known of all

Spad XIII fighters flown by Americans during and after World War I were the strongest fighters in combat; they could outdive any other fighter without shedding wings. But one incendiary bullet doomed the pilot to incineration—or a jump to certain death. (Air Force)

American pilots lost his life in an incident that resulted in great bitterness and controversy.

Major Raoul Lufberry flew brilliantly in combat, his skill so extraordinary that he became renowned among friendly and enemy pilots alike. During a great swirling dogfight, Lufberry dove his Nieuport fighter against an enemy airplane. No one is certain just when it happened in the wild melee, but a stream of incendiary bullets sprayed Lufberry's diving airplane. Suddenly it burst into flames. The other pilots stared in disbelief as the fire swept back into the cockpit.

Sometimes a man could save his life, even in a burning fighter. If he were low enough, or the fire had not yet spread back into the cockpit, he could chop his power and slip for the earth. In this maneuver, the pilot crosses his controls. For example, he would bring the stick all the way to the left to lower his left wing. At the same time he would push his right rudder pedal (or rudder bar) all the way to the floorboards. In this fashion the airplane would drop rapidly from the sky in a sideways–slipping–fashion.

Many pilots escaped in this fashion from what otherwise would have been certain death. As the airplane slipped earthward, the wind blew the fire away from the pilot. If luck remained with him, he had just enough time left in which to crash-land the airplane and throw himself away from the flaming wreckage.

Lufberry was one of those pilots who believed that, no matter what happened, as long as he could control the airplane he would survive. And he advised other pilots to do the same, to stick with the airplane. They might get burned by switching off the engine and slipping, but they would get away. "Me for staying with the old bus, every time!" declared Lufberry.

But when the time came, and the fire reached back to stab into his flesh, Lufberry did not wait a moment. He released his belt and stood up in his cockpit, and the next thing the other pilots saw was Lufberry's hurtling form. He crashed against the earth to die instantly.

After the loss of this great pilot, military leaders were blamed for failing to provide adequate parachutes for fliers. Some of the pilots referred to the Germans, who were carrying parachutes into the skies in increasing number.

No one recalls exactly when a German fighter pilot first saved his life by parachute, but it happened either in late 1917 or early in 1918. A German patrolling at high altitude— 22,000 feet, where the air was bitterly cold—was stunned at the sight of flames pouring back from his engine. In an instant the front of the airplane and the wings were a mass of fire. The German dove out of his cockpit. Wearing a parachute harness connected to a chute stowed clumsily in the cockpit, he dropped away from the inferno above him. The weight of his body snapped the retaining cord, and the German drifted safely to earth.

The first proof that pilots in combat were wearing parachutes came when a French pilot set a German fighter ablaze during a dogfight. Flames whipped back from the shattered engine, and the Frenchman watched—not without compassion—to see what would happen. Would the German stay with his airplane and burn alive? Or would he elect the clean death of crashing to earth?

Ah, there! The pilot heaved his body away from the terrible flames. But he didn't fall! The Frenchman stared in astonishment as a great canopy unfurled behind the German flier and then blossomed into the familiar parachute form. The German, in his delight at escaping from certain death, waved cheerily as the Nieuport circled about him.

This proved to be the German's lucky day. He sailed to earth directly over the front lines. The infantrymen did not know who—or even what—he was, and they blazed away at the helpless aviator. He fell to earth, after his perilous crossing of no man's land, with twenty-seven wounds from rifle and machine gun fire in his legs and thighs. French troops rushed him to a doctor, and he survived.

As the months passed, pilots were seen more often bailing out of their burning and disintegrating airplanes. Unfortunately, they were almost all German pilots, not Americans, or Frenchmen, or Englishmen.

Some parachutes were brought around to the Allied fighter bases, but the pilots hated them; they were sewn into cumbersome sacks and were big, clumsy, and much too heavy. The cockpits of the Nieuports, *Camels*, SE-5's, *Spads*, and other fighters were barely large enough for a man to squeeze into, and a man with broad shoulders usually found that his shoulders brushed against the sides of his airplane. When a pilot donned a harness and then dragged the parachute sack in behind him, he could hardly move. A few hours in bitterly cold weather, cramped and uncomfortable, was enough to make a man curse his chute and fling it over the side of his airplane. Worse, the big and clumsy sacks restricted the movement of pilots in operating their controls, and in the wild dogfights of World War I, agility meant the difference between living or dying.

Some pilots, however, persisted against these obstacles and carried their chutes into battle with them. Stories of how they used these chutes were passed from airfield to airfield.

The chutes were clumsier than anyone who had never used one could believe. To operate his parachute, a pilot jumped from his cockpit. As he fell from the airplane, the chute streamed out behind him, dragged from the sack into which it was sewn. When the pilot fell far enough from the plane, the canopy and shroud lines pulled taut and broke the retaining cord.

It sounded fine in principle, but it failed to work well in actual practice. For one thing, the system of releasing the folded shroud lines and the canopy could hardly have been more inefficient. If the airplane was tumbling or falling rapidly as the pilot jumped, the parachute streaming out behind him often snagged on a protruding part of the airplane. In other cases the pilot managed to jump clear, but the parachute, opening quickly as the wind caught it, wrapped around the tail or some other part of the airplane and dragged the pilot to a terrifying death.

The one story that brought most pilots to condemn the parachute designers and airplane manufacturers was that of a young French pilot. His controls shot completely away, he resorted to his parachute. The airplane whirled crazily through the air as he went out of his machine. In the tangle of airplane, man, and parachute, the end of the canopy snagged in the whirling propeller. Other pilots—friend and enemy alike—stopped fighting as they watched in horror. The Frenchman looped around like the end of a giant pendulum, drawn in closer and closer to the propeller blades, until the propeller finally hacked his body to pieces.

At war's end, almost all German aerial units were supplied with parachutes. Few Allied units enjoyed the same advantage, although the British had rushed into mass production their Guardian Angel parachute, developed by E. R. Calthorp. Unfortunately, it had the same drawbacks as the others.

There was no question in the minds of the parachute designers that some way had to be found to get a pilot clear of his airplane before the parachute streamed out to deploy fully. Yet they were not to solve the problem before the war ended, with hundreds of brave pilots and airmen dead, men who would have lived had their countrymen supplied them with parachutes upon which they could rely. The failure is one of the blacker pages in the history of aviation.

CHAPTER 4

The Parachute Comes of Age

THE OUTCRY over the lack of worthwhile parachutes for our fighting airmen began to produce results in the United States. Even as the war rushed to its close late in 1918, a small group of officers and men at the Army's McCook Field, at Dayton, Ohio, worked feverishly to perfect what pilots would unanimously agree was a practical parachute. Assigned to the Engineering Division of the Air Service were J. M. Russell, J. J. Higgins, Floyd Smith, G. M. Ball, and Major E. L. Hoffman.

There were no hard and fast rules for developing a reliable parachute, although everyone knew what pilots and crewmen required: a parachute that would enable them to abandon a stricken machine under any conditions, at any attitude; one that could be opened with no danger of the man becoming entangled in it, or of the parachute becoming entangled in the airplane. As part of the requirements, the Army specified that the pilot must be the one to operate his parachute; a system whereby a line attached from the pilot to the airplane triggered the opening of the canopy was ruled out.

To state the facts kindly, the military group worked almost entirely in the dark. Theirs was a procedure of trial and error.

There were plenty of parachute designs available for testing, and hopefully the Army people tried them all. They tested chutes used for jumping from airplanes and from balloons; they tested designs in wide use and others hardly known at all. None of them met the strict requirements.

No one even knew what material was best suited to making good parachutes. They knew, of course, that it must be strong, light in weight, and sufficiently flexible so that it could be stored for long periods, within a small package, and yet would open immediately and reliably when this was necessary. How big should the parachute be? The men could only guess. What shape should they make the canopy? Only one way to find out: drop chute after chute after chute, make comparisons, take notes, evaluate each one, judge it against the others, and slowly gain enough experience and knowledge to decide for themselves. Above all, the jumper must be able to operate his parachute manually, after he fell free of his machine.

One decision came quickly. Many men had jumped with cotton parachutes, but those seemed to lack the best qualities of the materials available. It did not take long for the small group to decide upon Japanese habutai silk as the best material. This silk proved extremely strong for its weight; it packed easily, was resistant to flames, and had a springiness that assisted in the quick opening of the parachute. Equally important, it proved reliable in storage and repeated use for at least seven years, far longer than any cotton material. Fortunately, it was available in great quantities.

The group sewed parachutes, packed and repacked their chutes, and performed test after test. This kind of work rarely is newsworthy, and certainly it does not make headlines. But most efforts to produce a product that meets everyone's needs are associated with painstaking and repetitive drudgery, rather than spectacular incidents. If a parachute was completely new and possibly unreliable, the men did not take chances. They threw dummies the size and weight of a man over the side of an airplane first to test the chutes and then, with these tests completed, made the jumps themselves.

Perhaps the greatest value in these experiments lay in the facts that were proven and the myths that were exploded. Most pilots believed that a man could not fall through the air without suffering injury or becoming panic-stricken. They believed that the shock of falling helplessly through the air would reduce any man to a quivering wreck. They said he would fall with such tremendous speed that he would no longer be able to breathe or to move his arms or legs. Because of these mistaken ideas on the part of the pilots—and many engineers, surprisingly enough—even the most fruitful experiments engendered little enthusiasm among pilots and their crews. They simply did not believe that they would be able to use their parachutes in emergencies.

We know today that most of these misconceptions arose from lack of knowledge of the characteristics of the air and of a body falling through the air. The greatest obstacle to developing the parachute proved to be this problem of overcoming the appalling ignorance of the behavior of airplanes and men in the skies.

Still, the small group persevered. The greatest hope came in a visit from Leslie L. Irvin, an engineer who had some startling ideas about parachute design. Irvin and Floyd Smith worked closely as a team to combine the best features of their separate parachute designs into a single new chute, and what they came up with raised the hopes of the Army group higher than ever.

The untested Irvin chute which resulted from their mutual efforts had a canopy 28 feet in diameter. In addition to the canopy, there was a small pilot chute that moved into the airstream first. The wind caught the pilot chute and jerked it away from the jumper's body, hauling out the rest of the main canopy along with it. The essential parts included the pilot chute, main canopy, the shroud lines leading from the canopy to the harness, and a pack into which everything went as a neat and secure package. When the wearer pulled a metal handle, this movement in turn allowed a steel cable to rip open the back of the chute. Perhaps *rip* is misleading, for the movement of the steel cable, the ripcord, withdrew pins securing the pack. The removal of the pins allowed powerful elastic bands to spring free. These whipped open the pack and ejected the small pilot chute into the air, which, in turn, was followed by the rest of the parachute.

If this parachute worked as Irvin and Smith claimed it would, a man could abandon an airplane, fall through the air, and then deploy the chute to save his life. But, as we mentioned, most pilots believed this was impossible. They dragged out all the old arguments: fear would freeze the pilot, the thundering windblast of the fall would batter him unconscious, he would be unable to move his limbs.

Despite the warnings of his friends and many of his professional associates, Leslie Irvin decided to test his new parachute in an actual jump. It was a do-or-die experiment. If the chute worked, Irvin would be a hero. If it failed, he might still be regarded as a hero, but he also would be very dead.

On April 28, 1919, Irvin climbed into the cockpit of a De Havilland DH-9 biplane at McCook Field. In the pilot's seat was Floyd Smith. Breaking ground quickly, he climbed to an altitude of 1500 feet above the airfield and then leveled off. Irvin loosened his belt and prepared for the jump as Smith turned at the far end of the field and came back at a steady 100 miles per hour.

Clusters of men stood near the hangars far below, their faces white dots as they stared upward. A hush settled over the men. All work stopped as the drone of the airplane's engine grew louder.

Fifteen hundred feet high, Irvin grinned at his pilot and stood in the cockpit. Then, abruptly, he dove headfirst over the side of the biplane. For 500 feet his body plummeted through the air, while men on the ground held their breath in suspense; as Irvin's body dropped to 1000 feet, one man cried out, "Open it! For God's sake, open the chute!"

But Irvin was in complete control. Just below 1000 feet, he pulled hard on the D-ring. The ripcord jerked free of the pack, the elastic bands sprang free, and a flicker of white—the pilot chute—sprang into view.

The next second, a thundering roar from the watching men echoed across McCook Field. Above Leslie Irvin spread a beautiful white canopy of silk; the jump was completely successful. On the way down, Irvin never stopped grinning. He came to earth so excited at the success of the parachute that he forgot to prepare for the impact with the ground. He heard a sharp *snap!* as an ankle bone broke. As he said later, however, it was worth every bit of it. One man reported that Irvin grinned all the way to the hospital.

Several days later, Floyd Smith also jumped with the new parachute and walked away from his landing. From that moment on, there was no stopping the little band of researchers. One by one, they lined up to jump with the Irvin chute; then other men, many of whom had jumped with more primitive chutes, arrived at McCook Field to try out the newest wonder in parachuting.

In his hospital bed, Leslie Irvin received with unrestrained triumph the news that the Army had placed an order for three hundred of his parachutes. The order proved an unexpected bonanza. Not only did it vindicate completely Irvin's theories, opening a whole new world of safety to airmen, but it began a whole new industry as well.

To produce that number of parachutes, Irvin would have to open his own factory. He could hardly wait to break free of the hospital to begin the work, and when he did, the new business began in earnest, continuing to this day. (The firm is known as Irving Air Chute Company—the added *g* results

The first practical manually operated parachute in the United States was first tested in 1919. Parachute experts state that it is very similar to the standard back packs in use today. (Air Force)

from a clerical error in preparing the legal papers for the business. In a great rush to get things under way, Leslie Irvin decided it was not worth the trouble to unravel the legal papers, and to this day he is known to millions of people as Leslie Irving, instead of Leslie Irvin.)

Two months after Irvin received his production order for three hundred parachutes from the Army, his name came into the news in an unexpected manner. In July, 1919, the Goodyear Company gained much public attention in the flight tests of its new and experimental nonrigid (blimp) airship called the *Wingfoot Express*. Thousands of people in Chicago craned their necks to watch the stubby shape droning slowly over the city, when suddenly the looks of wonder became stares of horror.

The *Wingfoot Express* gained its buoyancy not from the safe helium with which we associate blimp flights today but from the same explosive hydrogen that filled the sausage observation balloons used in World War I. As the blimp cruised across the city, there appeared a single tongue of scarlet fire. In an instant the rounded shape disappeared, engulfed in a roaring mass of flames that began to fall toward the city.

Seven men rode the *Wingfoot Express* on its doomed aerial journey. All these men wore harnesses about their bodies which, in an emergency, could be clipped to early model Irvin parachutes. The chutes were stowed within a cylindrical container bolted to the side of the gondola. If it became necessary to jump, a man rushed to the door, clipped on the main risers of the parachute, and hurled himself into open air. As he fell, the parachute pulled free.

Unfortunately, the disaster for which the parachutes were provided came with blinding speed. In one instant, the blimp sailed pleasantly through the air; in the next, it became a roaring inferno. One of the men in the gondola, Henry Wacker, proved to have unusual speed of bodily movement. In a blur he raced to the edge of the gondola, clipped on the parachute, and was gone. Only seconds behind him came the pilot of the blimp, John Boettner, who threw himself into space with desperate urgency and drifted earthward with feelings of gratitude toward his parachute. Wacker and Boettner landed safely in Chicago, but, because of buildings and other obstructions, both men sustained injuries as they came down. Neither of the two men felt inclined to voice any complaints.

Three of the five men remaining in the gondola also managed to escape, but their reprieve from death proved only fleeting. They clipped on their parachutes and, swallowed in the billowing flames, hurtled away from the careening gondola. But they were too late. The flames licked hungrily across their parachutes, and three bodies plummeted into the city, trailing behind them bright flames and thin streams of smoke. The other two men never even had a chance to jump.

The sequel to the ill-fated leaps for life shocked the nation. Flaming like a meteor, the heavy gondola and bag of the *Wingfoot Express* plunged through the roof of a Chicago bank. The gondola smashed its way into the mezzanine and exploded in a burst of flying wreckage and fire. Twelve people in the mezzanine died almost instantly.

The men developing parachutes at McCook Field pointed out that had the crew and passengers in the blimp's gondola worn the new Irvin chute, most likely all of them would have survived. Instead of wasting precious seconds in clipping their harnesses to old-style parachutes, they would have lost no time in leaping from the gondola. And the three men who did get out but crashed to their death, because of flaming canopies, would have landed safely had they worn the Irvin chute. They could have fallen well away from the flaming mass that overtook them and turned their canopies into fire, before pulling their ripcords.

Although Major Hoffman had ordered three hundred of the new Irvin parachutes, the Army brass withheld their official blessings of the new device. It was, to them, still an experimental parachute and would remain so until events or tests could prove beyond a shadow of a doubt that Irvin's design could not be bettered.

Three months after the Army placed its order with Irvin, they had their proof. A test jumper went out of a plane at 600 feet over McCook Field with the British Guardian Angel parachute. Shocked men on the ground watched the long canopy and shroud lines whip violently through the air and snarl the tail of the airplane. Seconds later, the parachute assembly ripped in two, sending the man on a brief and final drop to the earth. That did it: the Army declared the Irvin parachute the only device it would procure.

Continued procurement, however, did not assure widespread use. The decision to wear a parachute remained strictly up to each individual pilot and crewman; there were no orders requiring a man to wear the parachute. Some pilots still went aloft minus the safety that was theirs for the asking.

One year later, two men were to regret (however briefly) the lack of these parachutes. From the same field where test jumpers leaped steadily to improve parachute designs, a pilot and a gunner took off to test machine guns in the bitter cold of high altitudes.

No one will ever know exactly what happened. The men at McCook Field that day heard a deadly whine drifting from the sky. They stiffened where they stood or walked, then dashed out of their offices and shops. That whine was a dread sound on any airfield; it could only come from an airplane diving at full speed for the earth. And in 1920, no one dove for the earth from high altitude under full power, because no airplane could stand the punishment.

The whine built up to a scream as the wind shrieked through the wires and struts of the plunging airplane. Men looked up and shouted as they caught sight of a black dot rushing with furious speed toward the earth.

At 10,000 feet, the wings cracked and ripped free of the airplane. The great, tearing sound reached the men on the field; seconds later they again heard a ripping noise as the tail tore to shreds and broke free of the fuselage. They watched, helpless, as the body of the disintegrating machine fell, as a small figure struggled out of his cockpit onto the fuselage. And then that was all, as a plume of flame and smoke geysered skyward to mark the point of impact.

No one needed to say it. That man who climbed out on the fuselage—the Irvin chute would have brought him safely to earth. Instead, saddened doctors carried away his broken and lifeless body.

The testing went on.

Major W. G. Schauffler, Jr., 1st Wing Operations Officer, was equipped with two chutes for a jump at Kelly Field, Texas, on April 22, 1920. Schauffler is believed to be the first Army officer to make a premeditated exhibition jump. His reserve chest pack is simply a back pack, complete with its own harness, turned around. (Air Force)

CHAPTER 5

Higher and Higher

"THE PARACHUTE is a great thing," an early pilot mused to a group of fellow airmen, "if you're going low and slow. But that's all. If you're going really fast, you can't get out of the ship to use the chute. If you're high—well, the air is so thin you'll come down like a bullet, faster and faster, until very soon the chute isn't worth a plugged nickel. If you pull the ripcord at high speed, the shock will kill you. And at the same time, it will tear the parachute into very little pieces that will come down like snow but won't do you a bit of good— because by then you're going to be a couple of feet underground."

Most pilots felt the same way. Their ignorance of the atmosphere and the characteristics of falling bodies was overwhelming. For example, many people believed that a human body falling through the air always drops with constantly increasing speed. This is not so; the speed at which any object falls through our atmosphere depends upon the resistance of the air to the falling body.

A man falling earthward at low altitude quickly reaches his terminal velocity, the greatest speed with which his body drops. He cannot fall any faster, because at terminal velocity the resistance of the air equals the downward pull of gravity. This is a condition of balance, and the balance itself is affected by the size, weight, and shape of the falling man.

Under normal conditions, a man falling at low altitude (where the air is quite dense) soon reaches a terminal velocity of about 175 feet per second—roughly, 120 miles per hour. Compare this rate of fall to that of a man dropping beneath a parachute, somewhere between ten and fourteen miles per hour. Once again, the rate of speed with which the chute comes down depends upon the weight of the man, the type of parachute, the diameter of the canopy, and other factors, but ten to fourteen miles per hour is average.

We can never be exact, because the same man will fall at different speeds, depending upon atmospheric conditions. The falling speed is affected by the temperature and the density of the air, but equally as important is the position of the man and the characteristics of the falling body.

A man, as we have noted, falls at about 120 miles per hour. But this supposes his body is falling generally in a horizontal position, turning slowly and rolling sometimes as it falls. If the man can control the attitude and position of his body and drop through the sky in a clean, headfirst dive (as diving into water from a high board), he presents much less area to the air. This means less resistance to his fall, and he may drop out of the sky at 160 to 200 miles per hour. Similarly, a 170-pound bomb (the weight of the average man) drops at many hundreds of miles per hour because it is aerodynamically clean in its shape, compact for its size, and stabilized by its fins to fall cleanly and with arrowlike stability toward the earth.

Flat spins are a danger in long free falls. If a man spins rapidly at low altitude, his body begins to act as an airfoil—a whirling blade. Instead of dropping earthward with the average speed of 120 miles per hour, his rate of fall diminishes to only 70 or 80 miles per hour. The faster the rate of spin, the slower the rate of fall; rapid spinning, however, is dangerous and, under most conditions, fatal, as we shall see later.

The falling rates we have discussed apply to the lower zone of the atmosphere, where the air is rich and heavy and a falling man gains all the advantages of greater air density. Knowing that he will fall only so fast and no faster is a tremendous psychological advantage. The experience of thousands of jumpers makes it very clear that there exists absolutely no danger from a low-altitude fall through the sky.

It is most important that we clear up this matter, because many people still believe today (even with the sport of sky diving receiving so much attention) that it is a terrifying and dangerous experience to fall through the sky prior to deploying a parachute. It is just not so.

There is a world of difference between the jump of an experienced veteran and that of the man who goes out of an airplane for the first time under conditions amounting to disaster, his machine shattered or burning, his emotions sawed to a naked edge. The man who jumps as an emergency measure invariably begins his jump with a companion—fear. It is his reaction in which we are interested, and universally, it is one of amazement and surprise: the fall through the air is usually one of the most pleasant and enjoyable sensations ever encountered. Let us compare two jumps.

The first is that of Tony Levier, brilliant and talented Lockheed test pilot who has, in his career, twice gone out of airplanes. The first time the jump was deliberate. As a youngster, Tony decided to see for himself what were the sensations of falling from an airplane. He went up in the passenger cockpit of an old Waco biplane. At 3000 feet he crawled over the side of the cockpit, holding on to a wing strut for dear life. The pilot shouted "Jump!" Levier released his grip; instantly the wind swept him off the trailing edge of the wing. He caught a flashing glimpse of the tail, and then, "My first sensa-

*Not exhibition jumpers, these men are
part of an Air Force-Navy test team at
El Centro, California, testing chutes and
jump methods. Their controlled-free-fall
jump technique was first developed by
men like them in the early 1920's.*
(U.S. Navy)

tion was not much different than you get in a fast elevator or diving from a high board, but as I fell farther the wind pressure increased and I was conscious of the rush of air over my face and body. I had always dreamed of falling in my sleep many times and I was always frightened, but this was pleasant and not like a dream at all. . . . The next time I jumped was from a jet during the war, and it saved my life."

The next jump situation is entirely different. During World War II, in the Pacific, Lieutenant Joseph Daly flew wildly in the midst of a swirling dogfight. Japanese *Zero* fighters outnumbered the American planes. As Daly pulled into a hard turn after a *Zero*, another Japanese fighter arced around onto his tail. In seconds, bullets and cannon shells tore his airplane to pieces.

The instrument panel vanished in a blur of shattered glass and metal, flames roared in from the engine, and his clothing burst into flames. Daly jettisoned the cockpit canopy and dove frantically from the airplane. Almost instantly he felt relief from the searing heat, as the wind snuffed out the flames.

But remember the circumstances: combat, a blazing airplane, his own clothes on fire, imminent death. Yet, Lieutenant Daly kept his presence of mind. Like other pilots, he had been warned not to pull his ripcord at high altitude. Some of the Japanese pilots made special targets of airmen helpless in their parachutes, and so Daly continued to free fall from two and a half miles above the ocean. This is the point to note: that despite the terrifying circumstances of the jump, Daly did not lose his presence of mind.

He explained later that, like so many other pilots, he had wondered if he would be able to keep his wits about him and remember not to pull the ripcord. It all sounded fine in the classroom, and if you were an experienced jumper it might have been easy. But he had never jumped in his life, and the only thing that had driven him out of his airplane was the fact that he was starting to burn alive.

It proved fortunate that Daly did keep his mind sharp and operating "at full steam." As he fell toward the ocean, his body turning slowly, he saw a Japanese fighter diving after him. The *Zero* came out of its dive in a turning pullout, headed directly for him, the pilot obviously trying to set up a shot to blast away at his falling body. He said that the *Zero* "flashed past about one hundred feet away from me, but he had no chance to get his sights on me."

Daly's trial was far from over. He wore a seat pack, as do most fighter pilots nowadays. The off-center weight of the pack, as he fell on his back, suddenly whipped his body into a dangerous flat spin. And still Daly did not pull the ripcord! He reported that he was "spinning dizzily, rotating about the parachute pack, and, although I stopped this momentarily by kicking, the spin began again almost immediately."

Twice Daly came out of the spin; then, with the ocean coming much closer, he yanked the ripcord. He floated gently into the sea. Later that day, a rescue plane fished him out of the water.

This sort of experience lay far in the future when the small team at McCook Field worked steadily to develop the final parachute design that would go into mass production for all military pilots. The men who jumped did not have the benefit of these reports. They jumped into the unknown. Many of them made jumps under conditions that their fellow jumpers claimed were suicidal—and yet, they jumped again and again in the search for the reliable, efficient "silken angel" that pilots would be willing to take with them into their airplanes.

The most dangerous killer in the air then—as it sometimes is today—was fear. More than one person has jumped high enough above the earth to fall freely for many seconds and then pull the ripcord for a safe descent. But they never do. Instead, fear encases them in paralysis. Their minds freeze with fear, and so do their limbs. Or they simply give in to the terror that assails them and plunge from the sky, screaming, their arms and legs flailing wildly at the air. This has happened enough times to bring sorrow into many a test jump camp, because these are the men who know better than any others that so long as a man wears a parachute the best friend he can have is presence of mind. But not everybody is able to keep his senses about him—and some become victims of panic.

People falling from airplanes, with a parachute, have been strangled with fear. Their terror comes not from the effects or the sensations of the jump but from the very idea of leaping from an airplane and falling earthward. It is the kind of fear we can understand, of course, but the record stands very clear. The battle for life was lost before the jump; the person was overcome with fear before he left the airplane.

The most dramatic proof of this is not a pleasant story. A man who jumped from an airplane that went out of control left his airplane perfectly. He cleared the tail and fell cleanly away from the diving plane. Then he reached for the D-ring to pull the ripcord.

It wasn't there! Frantically he pawed for the ring. He searched in terror. He went wild. His fingers tore right through his flight jacket. He ripped his nails from his fingers as he went through the jacket, through his shirt, and gouged pieces of his own body out of his side in his wild attempts to find the lifesaving handle.

Then his body smashed into the ground, the parachute unopened. His friends were overcome with grief. The man who died never realized that the D-ring for the ripcord was on the other side of his body. He clawed madly at his right side, not at his left, where the D-ring just waited to be pulled. Had he caught hold of his senses, just for a moment, he could have reached to the other side—and lived.

In 1921, with the standard parachute of the Army and Navy still some years in the future, the little team of test jumpers at McCook Field wrestled with the problem of gaining pilot acceptance for their chutes. Not until the man died during an experimental jump with the Guardian Angel parachute did Army officials make their final decision to abandon any parachute design that did not allow for manual operation by the jumper. As we have seen, however, the order for three hundred Irvin chutes did not guarantee its inclusion as required equipment for flight operations.

The greatest obstacle to pilot acceptance lay in the area of bailout at high altitude. The reasoning of the pilots left little room for argument. At several miles altitude, they maintained, a man would plunge earthward like a rocket going straight down. Neither he nor his parachute could survive so wild a journey.

Not all pilots—and especially not all test jumpers—agreed with this idea. Sergeant Ralph Bottriell, a skilled balloonist, a test jumper, and also a very rugged man, scorned the claims of the pilots, but when he ridiculed their beliefs, they added one more problem. Even if a man opened his parachute immediately after leaving an airplane moving at slow speed, the air was so thin that the parachute would never deploy fully. Instead of a blossoming canopy, the pilot would have nothing more than a long streamer of silk behind him, and he would plunge with terrible speed to his death.

Bottriell said that this reasoning ignored the facts. If there was enough air at high altitude to provide lift and support a heavy airplane, that same air pressure would allow the parachute to operate as planned. The men argued fiercely day and night, their voices grew louder and their words angrier, and then they all concluded that arguments proved nothing. The only way to be certain that Bottriell was right, and the pilots wrong, was for a man to fly to very high altitude—and jump.

Bottriell squared his jaw and strode angrily into Major E. L. Hoffman's office at McCook Field. He would make that jump. His friends fought bitterly to dissuade him from his convictions, but Bottriell refused to budge an inch. Major Hoffman weighed the pros and cons of Bottriell's request. If Bottriell were wrong—well, the major didn't want the sergeant's death to result from his beliefs. On the other hand, Bottriell had proven a skilled and knowledgeable man. If he were willing to risk his life, the major would go along with him. He gave his official permission for the jump.

We know today that despite his skill and knowledge of ballooning and jumping, Sergeant Bottriell penetrated unknown areas as he prepared for his jump. During the preparations, someone suggested the use of oxygen bottles on the flight for Bottriell and his pilot, Sergeant Madan. Both men laughed at the idea, replying, "Where we're going there will be more than enough air!"

They were wrong. Bottriell planned to jump from 20,000 feet or higher, and there is not sufficient oxygen under pressure at this altitude to permit safe flight. At 20,000 feet the pressure of the atmosphere drops to only 6.75 pounds per square inch, compared to sea-level pressure of 14.7 p.s.i. But that is only part of the story. The oxygen pressure at this height is down to 1.5 p.s.i. We can translate this lowered pressure into more meaningful terms. The red blood cells of their bodies, which carry oxygen throughout the system, would be receiving only 70 per cent of the oxygen in the air they breathed. This leads to a condition of hypoxia, in which the brain no longer operates with normal efficiency. A man is unable to think clearly; he becomes dizzy and sleepy and sees spots before his eyes.

Most of us who have flown in jet fighters to high altitudes have gone through "flights" in pressure chambers, in which we are exposed to high-altitude pressures. A man wears his oxygen mask and then, to prove the point, he is told to remove his mask. It is safe enough, because trained men are right nearby with the mask. It does not take very long at five or six miles above the earth (or its pressure equivalent) to pass out.

Sergeants Madan and Bottriell, on the morning of June 28, 1921, climbed to a height of 20,500 feet in an open-cockpit biplane, without knowing the dangers they faced. But when the Lepare biplane had staggered to 20,500 feet, it refused to climb a foot higher—which proved to be a tremendous but unknown piece of luck for the two men. Four miles above the earth, the bitterly cold air struck them like knives. They shivered continuously, and their movements in their cockpits were sluggish and awkward. They could not understand why this was so, and they understood even less why they wanted to go to sleep. Their vision was blurred, and Madan could hardly read his instruments. They needed oxygen badly; they didn't have it, and it almost killed them.

Bottriell rose clumsily to his feet in the cockpit. The Lepare's engine, running at full throttle to hold the altitude, thundered at him in waves of sound. Bottriell shook his head, trying to clear the fog from his brain. He could hardly coordinate his movements. Then he rested one hand on the cockpit edge and leaned forward to shout to Madan that he was ready to jump.

He never spoke one word. As he leaned forward, he failed to realize that a projection in the cockpit had snagged the D-ring. Even as he began to shout his message to the pilot, the ripcord jammed on the projection as his body moved. The pilot chute sprang clear of the pack. The stream of air blasted back by the propeller whipped it away from the airplane like a shot. Almost at the same moment, the main canopy flashed open and disappeared behind the plane. In that instant, a giant hand gripped Bottriell's body and propelled him with explosive force from the cockpit.

The first that Madan knew of the unexpected parachute opening was an involuntary cry of pain. Under his foot, the rudder bar snapped sharply to one side and crashed into his ankle. Simultaneously the Lepare lurched crazily, as if it had run into a great and invisible obstruction in the air.

Even as this happened, Bottriell came within a split second of death. As the parachute jerked him from the cockpit, he instinctively flung out his arms to save himself—the attempt was, of course, futile, but Bottriell's movement was instinctive—and as he flung out both arms, the parachute smashed him against the tail of the airplane. For perhaps the smallest fraction of a second, Bottriell's body paused in its disastrous plunge; then it thundered *through* the tail of the Lepare. There came a blinding flash of pain as Bottriell's left arm sliced through the vertical fin and rudder, carrying away the upper half of the stabilizing and control surfaces. And then he was gone.

Madan knew nothing of this. He knew only that his ankle felt as if it had been shot with a bullet and, worse, that the Lepare had gone wild in his hands. The biplane skidded crazily, screamed up and over on a wing, and then shot earthward, out of control. A glance backward told Madan all he needed to know. Obviously, Bottriell had crashed into the rudder. Even as he realized that his friend must be dead—Madan had no way of knowing that the parachute had opened and pulled Bottriell out of the airplane—the pilot fought the airplane back to control and prepared to land back at McCook Field.

Another man would have died—another fifty men, perhaps —but not the tough Bottriell. Despite the blinding pain of his crash into the tail of the airplane, the sergeant retained consciousness. An iron poker seemed to stab deep into his chest as he fought for breath and tried to clear away the haze of pain from his eyes.

Clarity came slowly, delayed much more by the lack of oxygen than the severe pain. Bottriell looked about him. The world shifted in gray before his eyes until he realized that he drifted earthward within a cloud. Then the gray blurred

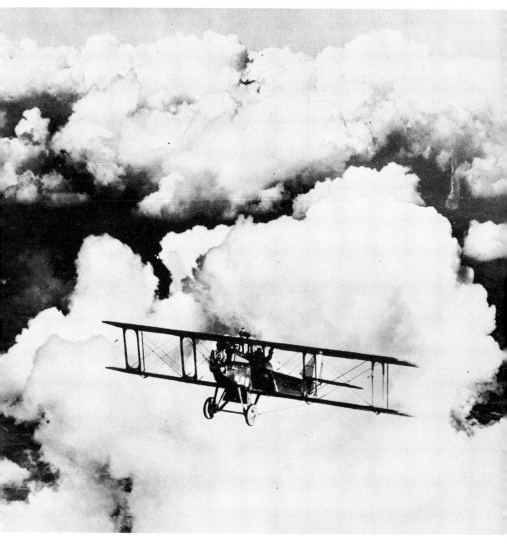

This LePere biplane resembles the one from which Sergeant Bottriell was ripped away by his prematurely opened parachute. (Air Force)

and bright sunshine filled the air as the parachute dropped through.

Bottriell felt a sensation of warmth running through his left arm. Puzzled, he tried to lift it; it didn't move. The sergeant leaned his head forward. For a long moment he stared at his arm. From elbow to wrist his flying suit was gone. From elbow to wrist the skin had vanished, and he looked at an angry, ripped, and bleeding limb. From the terrible gash, blood pulsed in a steady stream.

Bottriell realized immediately that if his arm continued to bleed at this rate he would be unconscious from lack of blood before he ever touched the earth; not only unconscious, but quite possibly even dead. Fifteen thousand feet above the earth, ghosting silently beneath his chute, Bottriell took the steps necessary to save his life, performing them in a manner that would leave brave men shaking their heads in wonder.

The blood flow increased. Gritting his teeth and summoning his strength for a mighty effort, Bottriell struggled to haul his body upward and into the shroud lines. With his right arm, he grasped a handful of lines and heaved. He moved upward, then fell back. Again he tried; and again, as the added exertion sent the crimson flow pouring from his left arm, he collapsed and fell back.

For a third time the sergeant clawed his way upward. This time—success. Working swiftly, Bottriell braced himself in the harness. He grasped a single shroud line, wrapped the line in a half hitch about his arm, and then collapsed back into the harness, the parachute rippling in response to the unusual movement.

By now Bottriell had turned a ghastly white. He gasped for air not only from the effort of applying the emergency tourniquet to his arm but also from shock, loss of blood, loss of oxygen, and cold. He felt his strength drain from his body; he became as weak as a child. But it no longer mattered. The sergeant's left arm stuck straight out, as stiff as a board, the weight of his heavy body pulling taut against the shroud line around the arm, neatly stopping the flow of blood to the arm.

In a remarkable fashion, Bottriell had saved his own life. He thudded to earth heavily in an open field, where the soft earth eased the impact of his fall. A farmer who ran to his aid judged the sergeant's plight. Immediately he knelt down and applied another tourniquet to his arm before running off to summon a doctor.

Later that day, Bottriell was driven back to McCook Field. There, in a joyous reunion with Madan, he learned that his arm had literally sliced through strong ash wood (two inches wide and three inches thick) to cut the tail of the Lepare in half.

There was another reason to celebrate the narrow escape from disaster: the parachute worked at 20,000 feet. That height had proved not so great as to prevent its complete deployment and safe operation.

Two months later, his arm healed in a long and ugly scar, the rugged Bottriell again was climbing into airplanes for his test jumps. But something was different. Sergeant Madan no longer flew with him. Thirty days after the miraculous recovery of the Lepare airplane, Madan's good fortune abandoned him. High over the Ohio countryside, whirling in a Sopwith *Camel* fighter plane, "something" happened to the controls. Madan spun tightly all the way to earth and died in the wreckage of his fighter.

One year after Bottriell's narrow escape from death, another man rose above the earth to prove that the sergeant had indeed been correct in his theories. Bottriell was alive, but the manner in which he eluded death clouded the success of his jump. As the pilots emphasized, a man without Bottriell's great strength would never have survived.

One of the greatest pioneers in high-altitude flight and in activities to be conducted at high altitude (there is a great gap separating the two) was Captain Albert W. Stevens, assigned to the Photographic Section of McCook Field. In the summer of 1922, he decided to better Bottriell's jump by at least a mile in height. Stevens listed his mission not as a parachute jump but primarily "to take photographs at the highest altitude possible with the Martin bomber." Stevens (tongue in cheek) explained further that coming down by parachute gave him "simply another way of getting down after the real work was done." Captain Stevens' own words of his record-breaking leap:

The weather had been cloudy, but June 12 dawned clear and bright, with a moderate surface wind. A few scattered clouds at about 8000 feet showed the upper air to be rough, as the clouds were breaking and suddenly separating into wisps of vapor. Our preparations for the trip included heavy clothing and face masks and parachutes all around. Three oxygen bottles were carried in the front cockpit; I carried two in the rear cockpit, as well as a 200-cubic-inch bottle for general use and a 70-cubic-inch bottle strapped to one leg. My parachute equipment was double, a 28-foot chute behind and an 18-foot chute in front. The small chute was not opened at all. It was for use only in the extremely remote possibility of the large parachute's fouling. I weighed about 250 pounds with all equipment as I climbed in the plane.

The ascent was quite uneventful, and I made negatives from time to time, keeping a record of the indicated elevation at which each was made. I started to use oxygen at 20,000 feet. As we got near the 24,000-foot mark, it became evident that we could not hold our position over Dayton; the west wind was blowing us east faster than our motors would pull against it. For some fifteen minutes we hovered around the 24,000-foot mark, now a little above and now a little below. The big plane rolled sluggishly in the thin air, inclined at a considerable angle upward, with the motors doing their best to put us higher. I cut over from one oxygen supply to the other and sprang clear of the rudder wires. It was very quickly over—in fact, Lieutenant Wade [the pilot] did not know I was gone until Sergeant Langham pointed my parachute out to him a few seconds later, far below and a quarter of a mile behind.

A sharp pull of the small steel ripcord, almost instantly a tug from behind, and my eyes, already turned toward my right shoulder, had a momentary glimpse of the parachute partly open, pear-shaped in appearance. A violent jerk followed, the merest fraction of a second later, and I knew that I was successfully launched.

The estimated speed of the ship, in the thin upper air with motors full on, was 110 miles per hour, and the eleven-pound steel oxygen bottle strapped to my leg was reluctant to stop when the parachute called a halt. I realized that something was giving way and made a grab for the steel bottle just as it slipped out of the lower straps, the upper ones having broken. I took a few puffs from the tube, but I was falling so fast that I soon realized I did not need the tank, so I tucked it under one of my shoulder straps.

Far above me, I got an occasional glimpse of the big bomber still fighting its way toward Dayton, but I soon lost sight of it. The chute rocked and tossed in the rough air like a wild thing trying to break free. Now it would be at an angle of 45 degrees to the north, then at a similar angle to the east, and instantly whip over to the west or south. After ten minutes of this, I began to get awfully seasick. The country passed under me rapidly, in fact very much as if I were being carried along in an airplane. Back of me was Dayton on one side and Springfield on the other; Xenia was off to the right. I could see perhaps sixty miles in any direction in the clear air. Ahead I noticed that my line of flight was almost exactly in line with a straight stretch of road leading into Jamestown. For a time I thought I would land near Jamestown, but such was the strength of the wind that I really landed five miles beyond the town, or nearly thirty miles from where I left the bomber.

I was miserably seasick, and I pulled the side of the chute way down to sideslip it and make it fall faster. The oxygen bottle had slipped from time to time, only to be pushed back, but suddenly it slid from under my shoulder strap as if it had been greased. I made a frantic grab for it, but it was gone. I looked down to see it tumbling over and over, until in a few seconds it vanished as a speck. Fortunately, I was over open fields at the time.

Now Jamestown was far behind me. I was getting within a couple of thousand feet of the ground. The air was still rough, but not nearly so bad as higher up. Ahead was a small forested patch of some ten acres. I sideslipped the chute to the right to avoid these trees. Now I could see my shadow traveling across the fields. Ahead was a freshly plowed field that I would like to have landed in, but the wind carried me over it. There was a single big tree, but I passed to the right. Then a barbed wire fence, which I was glad not to be swept against. Ahead was a grain field, with the grain some two feet high. The whole field rose at me with terrifying swiftness. I realized that I was going to hit hard and assumed a crouching position in the harness. Now, *whoof!*

Well, that's over! The chute whipped and billowed its silken folds along the waving surface of the grain. Some farmers appeared in the distance, but I had already gotten out of the harness and my heavy flying suit. They told me I looked rather gray for about ten minutes. I don't deny it; it was a rough voyage.

Captain Stevens' story omits some pertinent details, which only emphasize his desire not to make any more of his jump than there was to it. As Stevens fell away from the bomber, the thin air at his height (a corrected estimate showed the jump altitude to be 26,500 feet) affected the behavior of the parachute canopy. Instead of maintaining a taut surface, it billowed and flapped, alternately becoming taut and then folding in at its sides. The air spilled in and out as the chute seemed almost to be trying to breathe. And then, as the chute descended into the lower air and filled out, the oscillations from side to side made the chute behave, as Stevens described, "like a wild thing trying to break free." Neither did Stevens mention the severity of his impact. Later he admitted that he "broke a few foot bones" on striking the ground. Against the specter of a jump from five miles above the earth, however, this was a cheap price to pay.

The news of Stevens' jump flashed rapidly through the ranks of pilots everywhere. Now there could be no doubt that a man could jump at high altitude, in turbulence, and descend safely to the earth. Only one thing still remained absent to clinch the case for the parachute: no man with a manually operated, self-contained chute had ever jumped from an airplane in an emergency. The parachute had saved lives, but not in the case of a man who was forced to leave his machine in the air.

The pilots knew that the manual-operation chute would work in a jump from high altitude, and as an emergency device in the air. On August 24, 1920, a jumper arrived at McCook Field to demonstrate the new Jahn parachute. He prepared to take off when Army officials stopped him. He must wear an Army chute (Irvin) as a safeguard, in addition to his own equipment. The jumper (and the inventor, Mr. Jahn) protested this requirement, but Major Hoffman and his men stood their ground. No reserve chute—no demonstration over McCook Field. Finally they gave in. The jumper, a man named O'Connor, bailed out of an airplane at 2000 feet.

For 1500 feet he clawed desperately at the Jahn chute, but without success. The parachute did not open. Finally, only 500 feet above the ground, O'Connor ignored his faith in the Jahn chute and yanked the ripcord of the reserve pack. The Irvin chute blossomed immediately, and O'Connor dropped to a safe landing. Mr. Jahn was, understandably, very quiet about the merits of his parachute.

Still, the old argument came up again and again. Would the parachute work in an emergency, under the worst possible conditions?

The answer came on October 20, 1922.

CHAPTER 6

Jump for Life

IN THE FALL OF 1922, Lieutenant Harold R. Harris, twenty-seven years old, was assigned to McCook Field as Chief of the Flight Test Section of the Engineering Division, U.S. Army Air Service. Despite his age, pilots everywhere in the country knew Harris' name. Early in October, 1922, he swept the field in a major airplane race at Detroit. In 1918, he had led a major American formation flight over the towering Swiss Alps. And as a chief test pilot, he and his subordinates were responsible for proving—by actual performance—the merits of the new fighters and bombers that the United States Army would purchase in quantity. To top this background, he had also been assigned as chief test pilot of the Army's Barling bomber, then the largest military aircraft in the world.

On the afternoon of October 20, 1922, Harris' schedule called for an extensive maneuverability test. Lieutenant Muir Fairchild, Harris' close friend, would fly a Thomas Morse MB-3 biplane fighter with experimental tail surfaces. Harris would go aloft in a Loening monoplane fighter equipped with experimental ailerons, and the two pilots would engage in a mock air battle.

Fairchild took off first and climbed to 2500 feet, where he waited for the other pilot. But Harris was delayed on the ground.

"I had just had a new seat cushion installed on my parachute," he explained, "and after I took it out to my airplane, I found that the harness was a trifle tight with the new seat pad in place; consequently, I sent the timekeeper to get another parachute for me. The one he brought had an even smaller harness than my own; so after wasting considerable time trying to adjust the harness to fit my body, I almost yielded to the temptation to conduct my test flight without a parachute but eventually decided to wear my own chute, even though the harness was somewhat uncomfortable."

Harris was fully aware that many pilots simply did not believe that in an emergency a pilot would be able to get out of his airplane and jump, thereby saving his life with the parachute. He remarked, "Since January, 1919, while making thousands of experimental flights and testing hundreds of new airplanes, only two test pilots [had been] killed at McCook Field."

Nevertheless, Harris wisely avoided taking off without his parachute. When onlookers commented that wearing a parachute was a waste of time, because a pilot would be trapped by a crippled airplane, Harris remarked that it was surprising what a man could do when put to it. He had no way of knowing that soon he would put his own words to the test.

Harris met Fairchild at 2500 feet, and the two pilots jockeyed their fighters into position for their dogfighting maneuvers. Fairchild rushed directly at Harris, simulating a frontal attack with his guns firing. As the two airplanes swept aside to pass one another, Fairchild kicked the MB-3 over into a shallow diving turn. This gave Harris the opportunity to close in on the tail of the other fighter, to see whether it was possible for the MB-3 with its excessive speed to run away from Harris in the Loening.

The two planes sped along at full throttle, the Loening no more than 150 feet behind the biplane. Near the center of Dayton, Fairchild eased back on his stick and applied slight left rudder to enter a shallow climbing turn. The two planes were doing about 150 miles per hour when Harris cut inside Fairchild's turn.

"As soon as the turn started," Harris recalled, "hell broke loose." He said that the first vibrations he felt were exactly like the violent tremors of an earthquake. Then the entire airplane shook wildly from side to side. The experimental ailerons were unbalanced, and in the high windblast they fluttered up and down like two things gone mad. Their action immediately became so severe, Harris found himself helpless to control the airplane. Let Lieutenant Harris tell us in his own words of what it was like to be the first man in history to save his life by jumping with a self-contained parachute from a disabled airplane.

The only possible way I could control [the] oscillation was to slow down the speed of the airplane to such an extent that I could overcome the tremendous air force on the ailerons by my control force, so I immediately closed the throttle and started to climb. By this time, however, the aileron whip had become so great that the wing structure had been torn apart internally, and it was no longer possible for the wings to maintain their properly designed curvature. It was impossible for me to control the aileron action, as the wings themselves had begun to ripple in the wind and the aileron oscillations became extremely violent, with the movement of the control stick in the cockpit estimated by me to be about one thousand oscillations a minute.

The control stick movement was being stopped on each side of the cockpit by my legs, and if you can imagine receiving terrific blows on the flesh part of your leg between the hip and the knee at the rate of one thousand a minute, you will realize why three days after the accident I could not walk and for days suffered from severe bruises. My right hand, with which I was trying to control the airplane, was also badly bruised by the lateral oscillations of the stick.

As soon as I had determined that it was impossible for me to regain control of the airplane, there was only one thing to do in order to save my life. I have seen a good many airplane crashes. I have helped pick up a good many pilots who have been killed from various causes. I knew that in the event of collapse of the sort I was encountering it was impossible to land the airplane safely, and that if I stayed in the airplane I would undoubtedly be killed. I knew the next thing for me to do was to leave the airplane and open my parachute.

This was not as hard as it may seem, because the airplane was falling at an angle of about 25 or 30 degrees with the horizontal, and portions of the wing structure were beginning to blow off the wings. All that was necessary for me to do was to release my safety belt which held me in the cockpit and, in part, climb on the top of the fuselage. The tremendous wind pressure, probably 250 miles an hour, blew me clear of the airplane, and the next thing to do was pull the ripcord of my parachute.

I had never before made a parachute jump and had vowed that I would never, except in case of an emergency of this kind, since I have had the duty of piloting airplanes for about fifty live parachute jumps and in each case, as I watched the expression on the man's face when he was about to jump, I decided that it looked like too much of a mental strain to suit me. A surprising thing about the jump that I made in this case was that during the whole experience I did not become fearful of the consequences nor feel any faintness or failure of my faculties.

After leaving the airplane, I looked down at my feet to help my hand locate the parachute release ring and realized that instead of looking down I was looking up and that my feet were pointing to the sky and my head toward the ground. I located what I thought was my ring and pulled. Nothing happened. I looked again and realized that I was spinning like a top, my head down and my feet up. Three times I located what I thought was the release ring, but each pull simply indicated to me that I was pulling on the leg strap fitting of the harness which is about three inches below the ripcord ring. As soon as I realized what this was, after the third pull, I simply allowed my hand to travel up the harness or run down toward my head until I encountered the ring, which I pulled.

During this time my speed of descent must have been quite high, but at no time did I have any sensation of falling, and even with the extremely high wind velocity I had perfect control of my arms and could move them up and down my body at will.

As soon as the release cord was operated, I felt something snap within me and looked toward my feet to find that I was looking down at the ground. The first thing that caught my eye was a school building, from which a stream of school children was pouring toward me. I then looked up at my parachute—not with any sense of relief, because I had none. It all seemed part of the program that the parachute should open without argument, and I can remember admiring the beautiful silk of which the parachute was made. I could not understand how silk could be kept so white and clean, being packed under such varied conditions as our airplane test work calls for.

I then looked down again to see just where I was going to land. I remembered that the proper thing to do in landing was to pull one's legs up as if about to land on the ground after jumping off a high board fence. I also remembered that by grasping the parachute webbing with the arms, additional assistance could be got in retarding the shock of landing. The sense of relative motion between the parachute jumper and the ground is very small, and until one is quite close to the ground he is not sure just where he is going to land. I saw beneath me a number of small houses and some trees and had no desire to land in either, but I did not know what to do about it. A man was running toward me on the ground and at the last moment I saw that he would never arrive under a grape arbor at the same time I arrived on top of it, and that we would probably meet on the ground.

As soon as I saw the grape arbor I was very well satisfied, as I knew the frail laths of which it was built would easily give way and break my fall to the ground. This is exactly what happened,

Lieutenant Harold R. Harris was the first man ever to save his life by bailing out with a manually operated parachute from a disabled airplane. (Jim Greenwood Archives)

the only damage I suffered being a tear in the best pair of pants I owned and some cuts on my shoes when I went through the arbor. The brick sidewalk below the arbor was not particularly resilient, but I was not rendered unconscious by the fall, although my physical condition was low on account of the terrific beating I had received on the legs from the control stick.

CHAPTER 7

Caterpillars in the Sky

HAROLD R. HARRIS was the first man to be awarded a small gold pin. The pin startled observers, for it stuck on the lapel like a caterpillar. And that is exactly what it was, an exact replica of the diminutive creature who spends his life weaving the silk fibers which have meant the difference between life and death for more than one hundred thousand airmen.

Leslie Irvin started the Caterpillar Club as a sign of recognition to those men still alive—because of their chutes—who otherwise would have been dead. In the years following, other clubs were established, until finally the distinction between one organization and another faded into a blur. One point, however, remained clear. Any man who saved his life with a parachute could be considered a member of the Caterpillar Club.

Harris was not the first, of course; the two men who leaped from the blazing gondola of the *Wingfoot Express* over Chicago in 1919 could lay claim to that distinction. But people generally consider Harris the first because his jump was made with a manually operated parachute.

Surprisingly, the number of men who parachuted to save

their lives remained low. The year following Harris' brush with death, the War Department issued orders requiring all military pilots to wear parachutes whenever they flew. But giving an order and assuring its compliance is not the same. Difficult as it is to believe, even after Harris' escape the majority of pilots still mistrusted the parachute.

As word filtered back to the various flying commands that the pilots often ignored the orders to take parachutes into their planes and field commanders received instructions to enforce the rule, the pilots dragged the chutes with them to their cockpits, threw the packs down onto their seats, and climbed in to use the chutes as cushions. Disdainfully they refused to fasten the harness and roared into the sky without protection.

Shortly after Harris jumped over McCook Field, another man saved his life in a similar fashion. Lieutenant Frank Tyndall raced high over Seattle, Washington, in a swirling dogfight. He rolled and looped, dove and soared, and in the midst of the maneuvers he enjoyed so greatly he heard a terrible ripping, cracking sound. The next instant Tyndall watched the wings of his fighter plane snap free of the fuselage and vanish in the air. The plane lurched crazily and then screamed for the earth. Tyndall threw off his safety belt and leaped for his life. He made it. The parachute brought him gently to earth.

Although Leslie Irvin produced his new parachutes as rapidly as his expanding facilities allowed, it still required time to distribute the chutes throughout the services. The pilots, moreover, hated the discomfort of the bulky parachutes. Today chutes are packed into neat, easily handled units; in the early 1920's, the chutes were clumsy affairs. The harness left much to be desired, binding at the limbs and digging into the body. Since airplanes were designed before parachutes were invented, the pilots found that the chutes did not fit easily into their cockpits. A man accustomed to a glove-size fit in his fighter soured quickly on the parachute when he had to struggle awkwardly just to get into the airplane. He was further annoyed by finding that the parachute interfered with the operation of his controls.

The process of winning over the pilots could not be hurried; it was a gradual conversion, a shifting of psychology. As more and more men began to live through mishaps that without a parachute would have meant death, the pilots quickened their interest in the chutes.

For seventeen months after Tyndall leaped from his plane over Seattle, no other man in this country saved his life with the parachute. And then in April, 1924, a third member joined the exclusive fraternity of Harris and Tyndall. Bill Bottomfield wore no uniform. He had achieved a singular fame throughout the country for his daredevil stunts in the air as a jumper.

Bottomfield's specialty was to dive out of a plane at high altitude in view of a large crowd. As he fell toward the earth, he would open a parachute. Suddenly his body would slip out of the harness. As the crowd reacted in horror—men screaming and women fainting at the sight of a man falling to certain death—Bottomfield would yank the ripcord of a second parachute. He would slip from the harness of that chute, too. In fact, he would do this five times, until the crowd didn't know what to expect; did that last blossoming of silk mean the end of the wild fall from the skies, or was Bottomfield really falling to his death?

Bottomfield appeared a daredevil, but like so many other zany characters he approached his stunting with infinite caution. His five parachutes were his entire routine; he counted on the fifth to bring him safely to earth. But after these five, he had an ace in the hole—the Irvin chute, which he would never deploy unless it became necessary to save his life.

In the spring of 1924, the first five parachutes fouled together in an impossible scramble of canopies, pilot chutes, and shroud lines. Desperately, Bottomfield managed to rid himself of the whole mess and then gratefully pulled the ripcord of his Irvin chute. Thus he became the third member of the Caterpillar Club.

Before the year was out, the Navy was in. On October 16, Gunner W. M. Cole was flying a Navy fighter over California, cruising at 1200 feet. Cole was enjoying himself thoroughly, skimming along just beneath the base of the clouds, when the world caved in upon him. His plane staggered as though it had struck something, and then Cole realized it had done exactly that. Another plane came diving recklessly down through the clouds and smashed into Cole's fighter. After the first shock, Cole stared numbly at his left wing, but only for an instant; all he saw of his left wing was a blur and then the wing vanished, torn from the airplane by the force of the collision.

The fighter screamed down in a whirling, lopsided plunge, and Cole threw himself away from the tumbling wreckage. He counted to three and hauled away on the ripcord. With a cry of delight, he felt the opening shock of the canopy jerk his body around, and he sailed gently down from the sky to land on the verdant green of the Coronado Country Club. (Someone remarked that Cole was never so glad to break up a golf game in his life.) The other plane never came out of its shrieking dive. It thundered into the earth, throwing up a geyser of brilliant fire and snuffing out the lives of its two occupants.

From that point on, pilots looked with fresh interest at the parachute, and by 1925 the chute had found its welcome in the cockpits of airplanes flying the world over. Overcoming their initial mistrust, pilots turned gladly now to the device which had proven its worth by saving the lives of their comrades.

Two years after the War Department ordered pilots to carry parachutes as mandatory equipment, England's Royal Flying Corps (later to become the Royal Air Force) received similar orders. In England, as had happened in the United States, both young and old pilots greeted the arrival of chutes to their squadrons with hooting derision. They held to a simple philosophy. If the old plane failed you and burned, or fell to pieces in the air, that was the end of it, and no more nonsense. You had bought the farm, and somebody else moved in to take your place. Not only did they say this, they believed it. It comprised the bedrock of their philosophy as airmen.

But on June 17, 1926, the philosophy was shaken and the bedrock chipped a bit at its edges. Pilot Officer Eric Pentland sailed the air of the English countryside in a pleasant summer flight. It was "one of those days for flying," and Pentland wafted gracefully through the air in gentle aerobatics, swooping and rolling about without effort.

We can understand, then, why he "became a bit disturbed" when he rolled the airplane around on its wings and the airplane stubbornly refused to respond to the movement of the controls. What began as a gentle maneuver very quickly accelerated into a terrifying plunge toward the earth. The airplane flipped madly onto its back and then whirled, out of control, in a sickening inverted spin.

Pentland struggled frantically with the controls, but to no avail. Upside down he careened toward the earth, the horizon spinning crazily, the engine roaring, and the howl and shriek of the wind through the wires and struts reaching an ear-splitting din.

At less than 400 feet above the ground, Pentland abandoned all hope of regaining control. His hands moved in a blur. He released the seat belt and, in one uninterrupted motion, still seated in the airplane, pulled savagely at the ripcord. Pentland didn't believe he had a chance in a million of surviving, but the next instant a fist appeared out of nowhere and struck his body a tremendous blow.

Pentland believed the chute had streamed out and snarled in the airplane, but, stunned, he found himself floating in the air, drifting safely toward the earth. Ten seconds after he pulled the D-ring, his feet touched the earth, while 300 feet away flames roared upward from the wreckage of his airplane, pieces of which still dropped to the ground. Pentland could hardly believe it. He was alive and unharmed!

But not even this miraculous escape sufficed to break through the armor of British reserve. Sometimes it takes a grisly and shocking incident to destroy the beliefs tenaciously held by the many, whether or not those beliefs are valid.

The second man in England to save his life with this sort of parachute was E. Scholefield, a brilliant test pilot for the Vickers Aircraft Company. Only one month after Pentland escaped death, Scholefield raced over the countryside in a test of a new single-seat fighter. The airplane had been responding with thoroughbred agility beneath his skilled fingers when suddenly she broke free of his control and plunged like a thing gone berserk. One moment he was the master of the airplane; in the next instant the fighter screamed around in a wild turn, flipped through the air, and howled earthward in a fatal spin. Scholefield reversed the controls, chopped power, rammed the throttle forward, did everything he could to bring the airplane out of its dizzying drop. But to no avail.

Scholefield had never before worn a parachute! But, paradoxically, this day—the first time he ever lost control of an airplane—he was wearing one. He thanked the fates for his good fortune, pulled away his seat belt, and jumped. He landed without a scratch.

Two lives saved within one month made news. Every pilot in England talked about the miraculous escapes of Pentland and Scholefield—who was considered one of the greatest pilots alive!

Two years after his jump, Scholefield and another man roared aloft in a new twin-engine, high-performance airplane. Scholefield advanced the throttles until the engines roared with the thunder of full power, and the experimental plane leaped forward, accelerating rapidly.

Suddenly . . . a tearing roar, and the staggering jolt that turns every pilot's blood to ice. The two men turned in horror to see the entire tail structure of their airplane twist like a demon and then rip entirely away from the fuselage. Without the stabilizing tail surfaces, the airplane pitched forward violently. It fluttered and tossed to earth like the broken toy of a child. The two men went down with the ship. Neither man had worn a parachute that day. The object lesson was not lost on their fellow aviators.

From every part of the United States, and then from different corners of the world, stories came in of men who lived because of the parachute. At first the reports were a trickle, then a stream, and finally a flood.

Lieutenant Steve McClellan of the Marines climbed away from the Anacostia Naval Air Station near Washington, D.C., one morning to wring out a new experimental fighter. McClellan leaned back against a parachute that military orders required every pilot to wear. Clumsy or not, pilots were coming to accept its company in the cockpit with them.

Six thousand feet over the earth, McClellan cruised slowly. He took his time, trying all the controls, getting the feel and touch of the sensitive new warplane. She was a beauty; he could feel the power restrained in the engine and wings. And then, satisfied, he rolled the airplane over on her back and pulled the stick toward him, simultaneously advancing the throttle to maximum power. With 500 horsepower roaring in front of him, the airplane hurtled toward the earth. Steeper and steeper, until McClellan plunged straight down in a vertical power dive, punishing the airframe and the wings. His speed shot up to 300 miles per hour, and then even faster. The earth expanded rapidly in size.

McClellan's test was a maximum-power dive, straight down, and then the real punishment: he would pull back on the stick, harder and harder, until the centrifugal force of the pullout mashed him into his seat, drained the blood from his head, distended his legs, weighed him down with a thousand pounds and more—a painful, brutal way to fly an airplane.

But the forces working on McClellan would also be hammering away at the airplane. Could it withstand the beating? The Marine was there to find out.

The answer came quickly. A *crack!* burst from the wings like an artillery piece going off inside the airplane, and even as McClellan heard the sound the wings screeched in torment and ripped away from the airplane. At the same moment, the tail shrilled momentarily in a sawing vibration and tore loose. McClellan fell from the sky like a rock.

His trial had only begun. A small piece of the wing center section remained with the airplane, a jagged remnant of what had been a beautiful flying machine. As the speed shot even higher, the howling wind gripped this bit of broken wing and slammed it against the pilot's head. To make matters worse, the wing section remained over the cockpit, jammed in place by the force of the wind, trapping McClellan. The skilled test pilot wasted not a moment. He placed his hands against the wing section and shoved with all his strength. Miraculously, he raised the wing piece high enough for the wind to scream beneath it and whip the wreckage out of sight.

But time was running out, and the earth was rushing upward. McClellan released his belt and crouched low in the cockpit. He tensed his legs and sprang upward. Almost at the same moment the wind grasped his body and flung it away from the remains of the machine, the propeller incongruously whirling around at the front of a stripped and broken mass.

McClellan's body whirled through the air. He pulled the D-ring and was rewarded a moment later with a tremendous jolt that whipped him to a stop and set his ears to ringing. Despite the tremendous speed at which he pulled the ripcord, the parachute worked perfectly. McClellan splashed down into the Anacostia River. He was a mighty happy Marine when rescuers fished him out of the cold water.

Some men who abandoned their airplanes made their jumps convinced that they had no chance of survival, not through lack of trust in their parachutes, but in hard realization of the circumstances under which they bailed out. But as more and more men lived through aerial disasters, pilots began to compare notes. Their astonishment grew when they began to realize just how versatile an instrument the parachute could be. The stories of survival defied every possibility of a successful jump—and yet the men came walking back to their fields, grinning with the joy and relief of their reprieves from "certain" death.

The pilots quickly established certain standards for their emergency jumps. The word went around that unless you got out of your airplane at 400 feet or above—and opened your chute immediately—you met the ground at full speed. Everyone shook their heads in wonder when the story came in of Walter Lees.

A civilian pilot, Lees was flying cross-country near Dayton, Ohio, in an old German World War I LVG airplane, when without warning the controls jammed. Lees fought the stubborn stick and rudder, but nothing happened; the airplane streaked for the ground. Loath to jump, Lees stayed with the ship until only 150 feet above the ground, where it became obvious that if he wasted another second he would be dead. At this scant height he stood up in the cockpit, pulling the ripcord well before he cleared the airplane.

Seconds later, the crack of the opening parachute still echoing across the ground, his feet touched earth—safely.

Pilots returned to their fields with stories of how crumpling wreckage had jammed them in their planes, and how they fought and clawed their way to freedom. The number of men who opened their parachutes while still in their cockpits grew in astonishing number. Not all of them escaped unscathed; sometimes the chutes snatched them with terrible force from the close confines of the cockpits and smashed them brutally against the body or tail surfaces of their airplanes. They came back with broken bones and welts, with gashes and cuts and slashed skin, but every one of them professed gratitude for the parachutes. It was far better to have a broken leg, or even two, than to be dead, especially when death was so close that a pilot sometimes was only two seconds away from being smashed into the ground when the canopy blossomed taut! More and more the bullwhip crack of opening chutes, sometimes reaching the ground as hollow popping sounds, became a familiar sound.

The height at which men bailed out went steadily lower, until the time element between opening a chute and striking the ground virtually disappeared. No flyer could ever imagine an escape any closer than that of S. L. Pope, a British fighter pilot. Pope turned white when the sound of wrenching metal —and a stunned glance backward—confirmed that the entire tail of his airplane had ripped free. This is dangerous under any circumstances, because an airplane without its tail stabilizing surfaces sometimes tumbles so violently that it pins the pilot inside. Pope's tail assembly disappeared when he was only 800 feet above the ground. He struggled madly to clear himself of the wildly careening wreckage.

At 150 to 100 feet above a forested area, Pope managed to break free of the machine and, in desperation, yank the ripcord. For a moment he thought that he had failed in his bid for life; without slackening its speed, his body crashed feet first into the tops of some tall trees. But just as he felt the branches against his boots, his canopy boomed open with the sound

One of the rarest jump photos ever made shows a man only a second from eternity. Test pilot Ted Wells hit the silk moments after the ailerons ripped off this biplane racer in 1930. Wells got out barely in time and escaped with only a broken ankle. The parachute is just starting to deploy. (Photo by Harold Lyle)

of a rifle shot. Pope barely heard this, for simultaneously with the sound of the opening parachute he heard the noise his body made as it plunged through the trees.

Pope came out of what he called his "wild foliage rush" with a terrific back pain (which later disappeared) and some scratches on his ankles. That was all.

When his friends heard the details of his miraculous escape, they immediately sent off a telegram which concluded with the cheering words: "Forwarding clean pair of pants."

The survival margin in low-altitude jumps had narrowed down from several seconds to as little as a fraction of a second.

Survival depends also upon a combination of factors, all of which contribute to the final disposition of a jump—namely, life, or death. If a man leaves his airplane at high speed and low altitude, moving horizontally across the ground, he will travel laterally for a considerable distance. This lateral movement is vital to the jumper, because it can be translated into terms of time; high-speed lateral movement is equivalent to hundreds of feet in altitude, because it requires a similar time interval for the man to strike the ground after he leaves his airplane. A parachute can deploy in horizontal movement just as effectively as it does when dropping vertically. There is a great flow of air past the airman, and it is the movement of air that opens and deploys any parachute system. A man might be only three feet off the ground, moving horizontally, when his chute opened—and he would survive. This has happened to more than one pilot.

In the older airplanes—and the rule still applies today— pilots fought desperately for altitude before bailing out. An airplane bursting into flames right at treetop level can mean certain death to a pilot. But if he has a moment in which to haul back on the stick and send the airplane rocketing upward, he can win: he gains altitude; moreover, after jumping, the momentum of the airplane's flight is imparted to his body,

which continues to move away from the ground. Thus he gains
the all-important seconds that will save his life.

Not all the pilots who descended from the skies by parachute wanted to return to the earth in this fashion. Or, to put it
another way, some men who saved their lives by pulling the
ripcord never had any intention of leaving their airplane.

Airplanes at times are creatures of capricious behavior, as
every pilot knows—but may now and then forget.

Lieutenant F. O. Rogers, a Marine Corps test pilot, found
that a question of time could cost an airplane. Lest this confuse
the reader, let me add that it was a glance at a watch that
caused Rogers to lose his airplane—and almost his life.

Rogers took off one fine morning from Langley Field, Vir-
ginia, and climbed to 2500 feet. He flew for a while and then,
as pilots and other people often do, wondered what time it
was. The fighter planes of that era lacked the clock we find
on airplanes today; Rogers, not wearing a wristwatch, had to
dig in his flying suit for his pocket watch.

He unfastened his safety belt and began to try to locate
the watch, which seemed buried in a fold of clothing. As he
squirmed in his seat, one part of the safety belt slipped off his
lap and fell to the bottom of the cockpit. Rogers bent down to
pull the belt back. That did it.

The air was calm and clear, that day, but clear air turbulence can't be seen. Sometimes a pilot finds out that he is in
the midst of such turbulence only by the manner in which his
airplane reacts. This was Rogers' unfortunate experience.

The finely balanced fighter slammed into something in the
air. The next instant one wing shot vertically, the other went
down, and the ship staggered. That stagger, almost as if the
airplane had gone over a hard bump, catapulted Rogers clear
out of the airplane. One moment he was in the cockpit; the
next moment he was stunned to find himself sailing through
thin air. Instinctively he grabbed for the ripcord and pulled.

The chute blossomed, and a chagrined lieutenant watched his airplane fly about in lazy, erratic maneuvers and then dive into the ground. Rogers had some explaining to do that afternoon!

But the incident that made pilots roar with laughter occurred in Europe. A Yugoslavian pilot named Sergeant D. Ljumovich had gained a reputation of being absolutely unimpressed by anything he did in the air. His friends considered him a spectacularly skilled flier, but Ljumovich went about his business with an expressionless face. And no matter what he did, he seemed always to have a cigarette clamped between his lips.

On August 17, 1931, the sergeant pilot sailed through the skies, nearly 10,000 feet above the earth. Ljumovich loved to fly, and he loved aerobatic maneuvers in flying. He pushed forward on the stick until his speed built up and the wind whistled satisfactorily through the struts and wires of his fighter. Then, back, back . . . steadily but firmly he pulled back on the stick until the nose came above the horizon, continued to rise, and the airplane swooped up and around in a beautiful, curving loop.

At the top of the loop, upside down, the safety belt snapped. Very cleanly and without a bit of fuss, Ljumovich fell out of his airplane. A companion pilot stared in disbelief. No jerking of the body, no flailing of the limbs; there went Ljumovich, cigarette still in his mouth, out of the airplane.

The stare of disbelief turned into horror. The fighter airplane continued around in its sweeping arc, accelerating rapidly as it came down in a curving dive. The falling body of the man and the diving airplane met in mid-air. In an instant, the whirling propeller acted as an enormous scythe; blood spurted in the air as it sliced Ljumovich's leg neatly from his body.

Still squeezing his lips about the cigarette, Ljumovich pulled the ripcord. His friend continued to circle him as Ljumovich with incredible calmness tore strips from his flying clothes and fastened a tourniquet about the stump of his leg.

The other pilot dove at breakneck speed for the ground, rushing to his field to get medical aid for Ljumovich. No one expected him to be alive by the time he reached the ground, but Ljumovich, somehow, survived the impact against the earth with only one leg to break the fall. When they picked him up, white from shock and loss of blood, the cigarette was still in his mouth.

Ljumovich, by the way, proved just as indomitable as his friends believed. Several months later, he stumped his way to another fighter on a wooden leg and climbed into the cockpit. A few minutes later, he streaked off the ground in a hair-raising takeoff, having lost none of his fabulous skill. You guessed it: there was a cigarette between his lips.

CHAPTER 8

Heroes Reborn

THE AIR MAIL SERVICE in the United States began with a few dilapidated *Jenny* biplanes. The first flights in 1918 were akin to scenes out of Keystone Cops comedies, as the *Jennys* staggered into the air, flew perilously low along railroad tracks, and, every now and then, prematurely ended their flights with emergency landings on roads and in cow pastures. Air mail flying in its early days was marked by extreme caution. Commanders ordered their pilots to fly only during daylight hours, only when the sun shone or the clouds drifted high above the earth, and with an emergency landing field in sight at all times.

Obviously, this helped to assure the longevity of the pilots concerned, but it prevented any kind of scheduled service with the air mail. As the new program expanded, the government made available more powerful airplanes. Among these were the infamous DH-4 biplanes, which during World War I had earned the unhappy title of Flaming Coffin; a single stray bullet often transformed the De Havillands into blazing pyres that tumbled from the skies. The air mail pilots found little to cheer about with their share of these planes, for they were

The venerable Jenny *trained thousands of men and gave many thousands of aerial circus demonstrations around the United States. Its pilots often lacked parachutes, a fatal omission in an airplane that could burn like an exploding torch.* (Air Force)

generally poorly constructed, nightmares for the mechanics, and prone to explode violently during a forced landing.

Along with the new planes came increased requirements for scheduled flights. "The mail must go through" was not an empty phrase or a trite slogan. The government meant it, the Postal Department demanded it, and the pilots had to try and live up to it.

Flying the air mail quickly became regarded as one of the most hazardous occupations in the United States. Aside from the questionable reliability of the airplanes, the pilots lacked navigational aids. Instruments were crude, and the compasses, upon which any pilot must depend for maintaining a course, especially in inclement weather, were the bane of all pilots. They shifted and rolled unexpectedly in their sealed bowls, they jiggled and shook disconcertingly, and often the vibration of the engine tumbled them so that the pilot could tell nothing more from his instrument except that it no longer worked.

The need to sustain schedules meant flying no matter what the weather might be. Grotesque figures because they were bundled into their cold-weather gear, the air mail pilots slugged their way through storms, whitened in fear when ice formed on their wings, and writhed from cold sweat as they dodged and weaved a path between mountains and towers when fog settled thickly over the countryside.

The most hated of all the routes to fly was the one that crossed the Allegheny Mountains, the terrifying "hell stretch." It combined the worst of all the elements that can turn pilots' hair white. Storms built up on the western slopes of the mountains and then spilled over toward the east with unabated fury. There was fog, smoke, blinding haze, towers, peaks jutting into clouds—all combining to turn the Hell Stretch into an elongated graveyard for men and machines.

Here, finally, the parachute became the pilots' most important piece of personal gear. The choice was simple: a chance to live through a mishap or the prospect of certain death.

However, not even the parachute could solve the "problem" of the pilots, men dedicated to duty, who were convinced of the vital importance of getting the mail through. Despite cruel weather and the lack of instruments or lighted airways, they kept trying to fight their way through.

Many times they arrived at a destination to find that a landing was impossible; the field had vanished beneath fog or snow. The recommended procedure in this case was to climb higher and fly until the last drop of fuel had been sucked through in the engine. Then and only then, when the pilot had done everything in his power to get through, would he abandon his plane and bail out. Often the mailbags survived the crashes, since there was no fuel left in the airplane to burn.

Sometimes a pilot had to jump for his life en route. Over the mountains, in storms, the engine might quit; then the parachute was the only recourse. The numbers of wrecked airplanes and dead men climbed steadily. Many of the pilots tried to fight their way down to successful emergency landings. The mail—get the mail through. This was their creed.

Fortunately, most of the pilots recognized the futility of attempting landings in the worst of weather and under overwhelming obstacles. Many of them jumped and returned to continue their air mail flying.

Almost every American knows the name of Charles A. Lindbergh, for his sensational solo flight in 1927 from New York to Paris. But how many people know that this same Charles Lindbergh was the first man in history to save his life by parachute on four separate occasions?

Lindbergh's first two jumps came when he flew as a fighter pilot with the Army Air Corps. Later, as an air mail pilot, he entrusted his life two more times to the parachute on his back.

The first time Lindbergh jumped for his life, he was still an air cadet trying to win his wings. Out of the primary stage of training, Lindbergh then flew a World War I SE-5 fighter plane. On the day of his first emergency, he whirled through the air in a mock dogfight with another plane. Both pilots were skillful and daring—too daring. As they rolled and spun and looped, they suddenly collided.

Lindbergh stared death in the face. His wing ripped loose from its struts and folded over. In the airstream it flapped wildly like an animal struggling to break free. Every time it came down with a crashing bang, it slammed against Lindbergh's head. With great difficulty, he clawed his way past the flailing wing to climb out of the cockpit. For a moment he stood with his feet on the cockpit cowling and then jumped backward to clear the falling airplane. Even under the worst of conditions, the Lone Eagle maintained a marvelous sense of control.

"The wreckage was falling nearly straight down," he explained later, "and for some time I fell in line with its path and only slightly to one side. Fearing the wreckage might fall on me, I did not pull the ripcord until I had dropped several hundred feet and into the clouds. During this time I had turned one half revolution and was falling flat, face down."

Some time later, as a competent military aviator and test pilot, Lindbergh received an assignment to test an experimental fighter airplane. On this occasion Lindbergh came close to death, not because of what happened in the air but because of a decision he made on the ground.

Lindbergh walked to his ship, waiting on the flight line. His decision was to fly the airplane without a parachute; he was sure a chute was unnecessary. Suddenly, a superior officer ran up to the plane and asked about the lack of the chute. Lindbergh replied that he saw no need to carry one along. His superior told him to get his parachute. Lindbergh argued. His superior then ordered him either to wear his chute or stay on the ground. Lindbergh complained, grumbling about "stupid regulations"; when he took off, however, his chute was strapped to his body.

Several thousand feet up, the controls of the new fighter jammed. The airplane slewed crazily through the air, its engine whined, and suddenly the fighter streaked for the earth. Pilot to the last, Lindbergh fought desperately to regain control.

Finally, he went out. Only seconds remained as he left the cockpit at 300 feet. Even as his feet cleared the tail, he was pulling hard on the ripcord. The parachute cracked open, and a few seconds later his feet touched ground.

Lindbergh's third brush with death came as an air mail pilot. He was flying at night, outbound from St. Louis for Chicago. Nearing his field, he knew he would never make it safely to the ground. Over Maywood Field the fog was a thousand feet deep. Far below him, Lindbergh knew that men on the field had started huge gasoline fires and turned on searchlights to penetrate the wet blanket hugging the earth. It was no help. Lindbergh could see only blackness.

This rare photograph of Charles A. Lindbergh was taken aboard the aircraft carrier USS Saratoga *in 1936. Lindbergh was then a full colonel in the U.S. Army; here, he's posing with the three members of the Navy Sea Hawks aerobatic team.* (U.S. Navy)

Reluctantly the pilot turned gently to the left, taking up a heading to the west. He continued his turn until he was absolutely certain that Lake Michigan lay well behind him. Climbing steadily, he reached 5000 feet when the engine sputtered, coughed once, and went dead.

Lindbergh eased the stick forward, sending the plane into a gentle glide. It was marvelously quiet. Overhead the sky gleamed brilliantly with stars; beneath the wings, still that same thick, blinding fog. Lindbergh loosened his belt and dove over the side.

Several seconds later, he pulled the ripcord. The chute opened immediately; Lindbergh drifted quietly toward the obscured earth.

Then he heard a high, sighing sound that grew louder and louder. Startled, Lindbergh looked up. There! Silhouetted against the stars was his plane, sweeping around in a wide turn—and coming straight at him! Quickly, Lindbergh pulled down on one side of his parachute, to direct his descent away from the plane. With the wind sighing through the wings and wires, the pilotless mail plane flashed by, only a few hundred feet away. Lindbergh relaxed.

The sound returned. Alert now to its cause, the pilot stared at his airplane, returning for a second time. A bit more distant on this pass, it sailed by as a ghostly winged object in the night skies.

Three more times the airplane returned, dropping earthward in wide, gentle circles, swinging around and around the pilot in his parachute. Finally, the fog rose up to obscure the stars and the sky. Lindbergh listened attentively but heard nothing. He braced himself for impact with the ground. Still blanketed by the fog, his feet struck soft earth in a cornfield. Lindbergh rose, unharmed. He never heard his plane crash.

Several months later, the weather once again downed him. This time the danger came not in the sight-obscuring mists of fog but in a violent winter snowstorm.

Flying at night, Lindbergh tried to bull his way through a wide storm that grew in height with every passing minute. Behind him, other clouds had closed the route to his home field. He tried to fly beneath the storm, but at low altitude the snow became a blinding rain. He struggled as high as his plane would take him, but at 13,000 feet the clouds still reached a thousand feet higher. And then he was in the stuff, the grayish blur of snow a pilot recognizes at night.

Lindbergh fought his way through the storm until the engine coughed its last gasp. Thirteen thousand feet over the ground, he leaped into the swirling snow. The parachute carried him lower and lower until the snow changed to the thundering downpour he had run into earlier during his flight. In the darkness, Lindbergh crashed into a barbed-wire fence. The barbs tore up his heavy flying suit, but its weight protected him from injury.

That made four. Not too long in the future, Lindbergh would capture the admiration of the world by flying *The Spirit of St. Louis* from New York to Paris. He wore no chute on that flight.

Among the few men who are considered as the "greats" of the aviation world, James H. Doolittle stands near the very top of the list. Racing pilot, scientist, daredevil, precision flyer, fighter pilot, transport pilot, bomber commander, engineer, inventor, winner of the Congressional Medal of Honor: all these characterize rugged, famous Jimmy Doolittle.

As is the case with Charles A. Lindbergh, few people are aware that Doolittle, also, saved his life four separate times with parachutes.

Doolittle's first emergency came just prior to a national air race competition. Before the main race began, Doolittle took the new 600 horsepower fighter, in which he would compete, out over open country to test its mettle. High over the earth, he eased the throttle and stick forward, sending the tough little fighter into a dive. At a 30-degree angle, showing more than 200 miles per hour on his airspeed indicator, the wings failed. One moment the fighter streaked toward the ground, completely under control. The next instant Doolittle felt the airplane stagger, and then with a great cracking sound the wings ripped away from the plummeting fighter.

Doolittle admitted to close friends later that he really was *not* just in a dive. Instead, he had been punishing the airplane with wicked maneuvers and was in the midst of an outside loop (the pilot's head is to the outside of this maneuver, instead of inside in a normal loop) when the wings parted from the fuselage.

Regulations required Doolittle to make a "complete and accurate account of the causes of the emergency jump." Unimpressed by this official language, Doolittle was somewhat caustic in his report. When he reached "cause of accident" in the official form, he wrote, "Wings broke," and for a detailed "description of the method of leaving aircraft" he penned, "Thrown out."

The gyrating wreckage flung him away from the cockpit like a cannonball. Spinning madly as he fell away from the fuselage, he opened his parachute and landed without a bruise. An hour later he was back in the air, dragging another fighter through its maneuvers.

On two more occasions in his career he bailed out of fighters, and his fourth jump came on April 18, 1942. As commander of the group of sixteen *Mitchell* twin-engine bombers that took off from the carrier *Hornet* for the first attack ever made on Japan, Doolittle was awarded the Congressional Medal of Honor. Running out of fuel, flying into China at night, Doolittle kept his plane in the air as long as possible.

Then, with the tanks reading empty on the gauges, he ordered his crew out. Doolittle was last to jump, bailing out in pitch darkness right over Japanese lines. In the night, the wind carried him just beyond Japanese positions.

Fifty men jumped that night, not knowing what they might fall into (several men captured by the Japanese were tortured and killed). Of the fifty men who bailed out, forty-nine reached the ground safely. One man died in his jump.

CHAPTER 9

Aerial Adventurers

TAKE A SEVENTEEN-YEAR-OLD KID with more brass than brawn. Sopping wet, he weighs 145 pounds. He's just run away from home, he's hungry, and he'll try anything. The kid's name is Walker, Tommy Walker.

Back in the early 1930's, Walker dropped his skinny frame from a freight car he was riding south. The train crawled past a big open field at Orlando, Florida, filled with gay pennants, cars, hundreds of people, and a few ragged airplanes. It was a typical gypsy air show of its time. Walker ambled up to the fence and read a sign that the show was looking for an experienced parachute jumper.

Walker shrugged and muttered to himself, "Why not?"

The airport manager tried to throw him out, but Walker sneaked back to talk to the pilots of the planes. One flyer stared at him as Walker volunteered for the job. "You're a jumper?" he asked incredulously.

"Hell, yes," Walker answered blandly. "I've had lots of experience."

"What kind of chutes you jump with?" the pilot asked.

"Any kind."

The pilot shook his head, then shrugged. "Okay, kid," he said. "You're on. Let's see how you can do."

They helped him into the harness of a seat-pack chute. Walker was grateful for the assist, for he had no idea of how to wear a parachute. He had never worn one before—in fact, he had never even seen a parachute before—and to top off a resounding lack of experience, he had never been in the air!

Fifteen minutes later, Walker gazed in fascination from the cockpit of an old Fleet biplane as the earth fell away. Then the pilot ordered him out onto the wing. Walker climbed out, clumsy in the chute, clumsier in the 70-mile-per-hour wind. Down below—2000 feet below—the field looked like a postage stamp.

Walker had only one chute. He didn't even know what the term *emergency chute* meant. He clung grimly to the wing strut.

"Hey, kid!" the pilot shouted. "You ain't scared, are you?"

"Hell, no!" Walker shouted back. Then, to himself, "You gotta start sometime." He released his grip.

The wing whirled before his eyes as the wind flipped him into space. Walker tumbled as he fell, startled at the sight of the horizon spinning around. He counted to five, shut his eyes, and yanked on the D-ring.

His harness was not tightly fastened to his skinny frame. As the chute boomed open, Walker saw blazing stars. A hundred fists slammed into his body; then all of a sudden the horizon and the earth went back to where they belonged. Walker blinked and uttered a relieved, "Whew!"

Abruptly, his entire attitude changed. He forgot the ebbing pain. He had slipped into that marvelous world of being suspended in space. It was the most wonderful sensation he had ever known, and, from that moment on, Herbert M. C. Walker— Tommy to his friends—was committed to a life in the air. It was to be (and still is) a fantastic lifetime of flying skill and courage, of a man who has been described as fearless.

I know, for Tommy Walker is a close friend of mine and, as well, the man who taught me to fly.

Walker went on from the sudden revelation of his first flight and first parachute jump to become one of the world's most skillful pilots, a devil-may-care soldier of fortune who has never once turned down what promised to be a good fight. His flying has subjected him to burns, gunshot wounds, gashes, cuts, bruises, broken bones, and scalding. He has fought in a couple of wars, and he became a daring stunt flyer who merrily crashed airplanes into barns, poles, walls, locomotives, and other assorted items that stopped his plane with bruising force.

All this, of course, was to follow that first terrifying, exhilarating jump which ended with sweet words. Walker dropped to the airfield, landed hard, rolled over, and jumped to his feet with an air of aplomb that smacked of long experience at leaping into thin air. The other two barnstormer pilots ran to his side. One of them called out, "Okay, kid! You're hired!"

Walker grinned at him.

During his career as a stunt man, wing-walker, crash expert, fighter pilot, bomber pilot (Walker is qualified to fly almost every type of airplane in the world), he also went on to become a master jumper. As a stunt jumper he leaped from airplanes more than three hundred and sixty times. He developed some of the zaniest routines in air shows. Walker liked to go out of a plane at 12,000 to 15,000 feet, wearing either a convict's uniform or a pair of bathing trunks. And as he plummeted earthward, always under perfect control, he would blow loudly on a bugle!

But stunt jumping stories are not for this book. I have described Tommy Walker's background only to show this man's hectic and adventurous career. The point here is that there were three times during this career when Walker's luck ran out, and a parachute worn specifically for emergency purposes saved his life.

To Tommy Walker, the jumps he made as a stunt man at air

shows and fairs were just part of the game. "Hell, lots of guys jumped," he explains, "and many of them were fabulous. Take Art Starnes, for example. He used to wear pants with layers of leather pads sewn into the seat. He'd hang on to the bottom of a plane, the pilot would drop down to just above the ground, and at sixty-five miles per hour, old Art would let go. That was the damndest sight you ever saw—Art screeching across the field at sixty-five miles per hour on his butt. The crowd used to howl at that.

"Well, Art was also a great jumper. There were dozens of guys who were great. Stunt jumping was the way we lived—or a part of the way we lived. Those other three jumps were sorta special. I had no intention of going out, but it was either that or die. When you get right down to it, they were *very* special. Without a chute each time, it would have been the end of the road."

Tommy Walker at one time flew with a group of barnstormers in a hectic, wild, and uproarious tour of the country. He worked with the group as pilot, wing-walker, crash artist, and jumper. And then the crowds ran out and the money was gone. The group decided to break up.

One of the pilots had a smuggling deal going between Mexico and the United States, and he invited Walker in. He jumped at the chance. It was money. But above all, it meant flying.

The pilot didn't know what his contraband cargo was, he didn't care, and he never asked. Life remained much healthier with that attitude. He asked no questions but ran his delivery service as agreed. From Houston, Walker and his new partner flew to a farmer's pasture near El Paso, Texas, where their contact delivered the cargo.

It was a good life, with a thousand dollars to split up for every trip. After several weeks, however, their success gained notice. The Mexican *rurales* chafed at their inability to catch the smugglers.

Walker and his friend didn't help matters with their conduct. On the ground, Walker was uproariously drunk half the time, but in the air, as sober as a judge—always.

His friend proved to be worse. He got drunk on the ground, he was drunk before a flight, and most of the time he was drunk in the air. It was just this—his playful disposition in the air, when he could hardly walk up to the airplane before take-off—that finally proved their undoing.

One night they hedgehopped over the border, wheels barely skimming the brush. The moon shone brightly in clear skies, and the two pilots were having the time of their lives. The desert flashed beneath them, and the propeller hurled back a long spray of dust into the air, rising behind the airplane as they sped along.

Under that silvery moon, the pilots spotted a Mexican border patrol. They were not there by accident; the Mexicans were looking for the phantom airplane. Walker's friend stared through alcohol-glazed eyes. No one was going to push *him* around. He hauled back on the stick, stamping on a rudder pedal; the old *Travelair* clawed around in a tight, climbing turn. And then it was coming back down again, engine screaming under full throttle, as the pilot dove at full speed directly into the horsemen to scatter them.

The Mexicans did not flinch. From their saddles they poured a steady barrage of rifle fire into the biplane. Finally a bullet smashed into a control cable as the plane swooped upward. The pilots were only 200 feet up when the ship lurched crazily and whipped into a flat spin.

"It was wild," Walker explained to me. "We had to get our belts free, climb out, and jump. That isn't easy when a plane is berserk beneath you. The spin hangs on to you like you're stuck on a big sheet of flypaper. But somehow we got out of the cockpits, and I know I didn't jump. I threw myself out, yanking on the ripcord, I think, while my feet were still clearing the ship. The other pilot did the same thing. He sure sobered up in a hurry! We both made it down okay; the desert was soft and we didn't get hurt, although I think we hit the ground only one or two seconds after the canopies deployed. While it was still dark, we sneaked back across the border. The Mexicans gave us a good head start. They figured we went in with the ship, and since it burned for a while after crashing, we were gone by the time they figured it out."

That was 1932. Five years later, Walker again jumped for his life. This time the locale was China. Walker flew for Claire Chennault's old Foreign Legion, made up of soldiers of fortune from all over the world who had come to join Chennault in fighting the Japanese. (The Flying Tigers didn't enter combat until December 22, 1941.)

The Chinese gave Walker a weather-beaten Curtiss *Hawk III* fighter, a weary biplane with single .30- and .50-caliber machine guns, each firing through the propeller. With a 750-horse-power Cyclone engine, Walker could hit up to 215 miles per hour in the old fighter. It was not nearly fast enough; the Japanese could fly circles around an airplane with that slow speed. But how she could maneuver! To Walker she was a dream, weary wings and all.

That maneuverability, and Walker's experience as a stunt and aerobatic pilot, more than once saved his life. Many times he and the other pilots dove pellmell after Japanese bombers, but their Mitsubishi 96 fighter escort almost always cut in between the diving *Hawk* biplanes and the bomber formations. The Japanese fighters outnumbered the little band of *Hawks*.

"In man-to-man fights," Walker relates, "we could whip the Japanese pilots. But in a big melee, outnumbered, fighting against superior planes, we hardly stood a chance. If we could dive in against the bombers or even the fighters, using all the speed from the dive, we could cut them up. In fact, I got two kills in attacks like these. But don't let me mislead you. Many times we had no choice but to run for our lives."

In the Nanking area one day, with three other *Hawks*,

Walker and the other pilots were bounced—but good. Ten Mitsubishi fighters came diving out of the sun, and they hit the four-plane formation like an avalanche. It was a slaughter. Two of the *Hawks* went down almost at once, the airplanes riddled and the pilots dead.

Walker and another pilot barreled around in desperate turns, trying to bring their guns to bear on the Japanese planes. Walker's wingman poured a burst into the tanks of one Mitsubishi, exploding the airplane in flames. Almost at the same moment, his own plane vanished in a searing ball of fire.

His plane a shattered wreck, Walker twisted and weaved like a madman. It gained him only a few seconds. The Mitsubishis cut him to pieces, and then flames licked back from the shattered engine. Still the Japanese pilots stayed with him, pouring bullets into the disintegrating, burning fighter.

Walker stood the fire as long as he could. Then, when the flames were lashing against his skin, the engine exploded in a great flaming blast. Over the Chinese lines he bailed out. Behind him, the Mitsubishis swooped down in curving dives, waiting for the sign of his parachute to open fire.

"My stunt jumping saved my life," Walker explains. "I could judge carefully just when to open the chute. I waited until I was about five or six hundred feet up and hauled on the D-ring. I don't think I was more than fifty to a hundred feet off the ground when the canopy deployed fully. I made it out of the harness and into thick brush before the Japs could gun me down. All in all, it was quite a day."

Three years later, Walker once again found it imperative to abandon an airplane in an emergency. In 1940 he was at an Oregon aircraft plant as a test pilot. On the field was a new Stinson 105 private plane. The new ship had been so designed that its inherent stability resisted spinning (a stall in which the airplane rotates rapidly and falls from the sky). One of the engineers said flatly that, no matter what mistakes a pilot might make, the airplane would not go into a spin.

Walker snorted at this remark. The engineers argued. Walker shot back that there wasn't a plane in the world that couldn't be made to spin. The conclusion of the argument was an order for Walker to "do your best to spin that thing."

He did his best, and it was much better than most! He brought the Stinson into proper position, slammed expertly at the controls, and the next moment the Stinson whirled for the ground—spinning. Walker had to admire the engineer, because he had to work to keep the airplane in the spin. But then, at 2000 feet, a great screeching sound diverted his attention. He looked back; the entire tail of the airplane had ripped loose on one side and flapped crazily in the air.

Walker had no rudder to come out of the spin. The cable had severed. But he still had elevator control. He popped the stick forward and then back; the Stinson shuddered out of the dive, banging and crashing in its tail section. Walker slowed the airplane to just above stalling speed, forced open the cabin door, and dove for safety—the safety of his parachute. That was his third Caterpillar Club jump.

One final incident in the Walker story must be told. In 1941 he returned to his first love, the air show. A telegram to an old friend, Dutch Wendt, brought his buddy out to the west coast, where the two men formed a stunt team.

With Dutch, Walker did his first double jump. Gripping one another tightly, the two men tumbled out of a plane at 5000 feet. Dutch was to open his chute first. Then Tommy Walker would fall away into space, jerking his ripcord just above the crowd.

Fortunately for Dutch, he was to begin the act. At 4000 feet he jerked the ripcord—but the chute wouldn't open! He screamed to Walker, "Hold on tight to me, you son of a bitch! Hold on *tight!*"

Grasping his friend, Walker plummeted with Dutch, climbing around to his back in an attempt to get the chute out.

Nothing happened. The earth rushed up at them.

"Hang onto the straps!" Walker shouted. "I'm going to open my chute!"

Dutch gripped him tightly, as Walker's hand jerked the ring. Their double weight nearly proved their end. There was a tremendous smacking noise as the silk inflated, and then a booming *crack!* as several panels ripped open. The shock slammed Dutch unconscious, and as his body tore away, a suspension line raked Walker's ear, tearing it open. Blood spurted, but Walker ignored it, staring in horror as the unconscious Dutch fell toward the earth.

And then, miraculously—silk! The wind had pulled the parachute from Dutch's pack where Walker had yanked desperately to free it. Dutch was still unconscious when he reached the ground on the bank of a river. Walker landed smack in the middle of the river and was rescued by a man and woman fishing in a motorboat. His ear still streamed blood, but a grin split his face from ear to ear. Why not, after that kind of a close call?

Although most parachute jumps conclude exactly as the jumpers had planned (and hoped), sometimes what begins as an ordinary jump under perfect conditions quickly becomes a hair-raising adventure. Two cases deserve our special attention. Women were involved in both these separate but remarkably similar incidents.

The first story involves Major Hoffman, the officer who commanded the small group of parachutists at McCook Field who helped develop the first official military parachute, the Type S, developed from Irvin's experimental pack.

At the close of a full day of stunt and exhibition flying at Grissard Field (a government reserve airport), Mrs. Irene MacFarland was scheduled to end the show with a parachute drop from 3500 feet. It was to be her second jump of the day; she had made a practice jump early that morning.

For some reason, perhaps economy, Irene MacFarland still

Herbert "Tommy" Walker—fighter and bomber pilot, veteran of at least three air forces, aerobatic pilot, stunt man, wing-walker, parachutist extraordinary, test pilot—is one of the most skilled men in aviation today. (Martin Caidin Archives)

jumped with the old type of parachute made of canvas. She wore a harness, but instead of a pack the shroud lines ran to the parachute stowed into a bag lashed to the axle of the landing gear. When she fell away from the airplane, the weight of her body was to pull the chute free of its container, opening it immediately. Irene MacFarland had full confidence in the chute; no one but her husband ever packed it.

But Major Hoffman did not share this confidence. After taking one look at the clumsy arrangement, the major ordered Mrs. MacFarland to wear a Government Type S parachute as an emergency pack. Mrs. MacFarland protested; her husband shouted; the major insisted. Regulations required anyone, military or civilian, flying from a government field to wear the Irvin chute. The argument waxed hotly, but Hoffman remained adamant; either she wore the Irvin chute or she didn't fly from this airfield!

Irene MacFarland took off, wearing the Type S parachute and her own harness. At 3500 feet, her drop airplane swung around for its final, steady pass high over the massed throng below. Irene MacFarland climbed to the edge of the cockpit, waved, and then jumped.

She did not get very far. In fact, her body only dropped several feet and then jerked cruelly to a stop. She swung helplessly from the airplane, dangling and whipping in the wind at the end of a rope, helpless to regain the airplane.

The parachute bag on the axle was so made that the mouth of the bag was woven together to leave a small space through which the canvas canopy would deploy. Linen tape prevented the chute from opening inadvertently in the wind; as the jumper's weight pulled against the linen tape, it was supposed to split, allowing the chute to come out freely.

Someone—perhaps Mr. MacFarland—had done too good a job. The tape proved so strong that not even the weight of the woman's body in the high wind was great enough to snap or pull it away, and Irene MacFarland ended up in one of the most dreaded positions of all, swinging and rocking wildly like a pendulum gone berserk.

The pilot stared helplessly at her white and frightened face. He signaled frantically for her to pull the D-ring of the Irvin chute. For several moments she failed to understand his message. The pilot rose in his seat, pointing clearly to his own D-ring, motioning again for her to pull the ripcord.

Mrs. MacFarland could barely nod her head in assent in the screaming wind. But she brought her hand up, clasped the ring, and jerked with all her strength. Instantly the pilot chute snapped free, and then the silken white canopy blossomed out.

But Irene MacFarland was not safe yet. The opened parachute might break her free of the airplane—or the airplane might be whipped around into an uncontrollable spin. Everyone stared from the ground, helpless, filled with dread at what might happen.

The opened canopy pulled with tremendous force at the body swinging from the airplane. A loud *snap!* was heard as the canvas parachute broke free. But the wildly flapping canopy whirled through the air, blew back, and snarled the tail of the airplane!

Desperately, the pilot shoved the throttle forward and hauled back on the control stick to send the airplane into a steep climb, trying to break the chute free. The airplane lurched suddenly, the tail shot up: it worked! The parachute slipped away from the airplane, blossomed out, and Mrs. MacFarland was on her way to the ground in safety.

The folds of the exhibition chute fluttered uselessly to the ground.

Another woman who had a similar experience, but who suffered a great deal more and faced almost certain death, was a professional aerial circus performer. Rosalie Gordon was a "pretty gal" and a sharp stuntwoman. On April 10, 1931, Miss Gordon went aloft for an exhibition jump, her first jump. Flying the airplane was Clyde E. Pangborn, one of the greatest flying pioneers of all time (late in 1931 he became the first man to fly nonstop from Japan to the United States mainland). Rosalie Gordon tells her story in her own words:

I was mascot of the 36th Division, Air Service, and in an exhibition to be given for the benefit of the Reserve Fund, I offered to do a parachute jump. I had been wing-walking several years, but this was to be my first jump. I was given a Harding Exhibition parachute, balloon bell pack, with a small rope around the end pack. Just before I went up, it had been raining heavily, and as soon as the rain stopped a picture concern asked permission to take a picture of me with my parachute.

Though I did not know it at the time, subjecting the parachute to the damp weather had caused the ropes holding the ring of the parachute to shrink, and the ring then could not release the bag. Clyde Pangborn was piloting the plane in which I went up, and Captain Milton Girton sat in the cockpit with me. When the plane had ascended to the height of 4000 feet, the signal was given, and I jumped overboard. It was pouring down rain, having started again just after I left the airplane.

Then, for a terrible minute, I realized that my chute had not opened! Momentary panic was replaced by the conviction that I must do all I could to save my life; meanwhile, Captain Girton, aware of my predicament, leaned over and began hauling up the rope that linked me to the airplane. But his strength proved inadequate, and when he had to release the rope I dropped again. Then the pilot, Clyde Pangborn, dived for the ground and took me across the field about eighteen feet off the ground to appeal for help. Several were determined to lend aid, among them Lieutenant Strickland, who was stationed at Kelly Field, flying a Morse machine; Tommy Thompson, a civilian pilot, taking Freddie Lund, my teacher and sponsor; Lieutenant Lewis Gross, Air Reserve; and Major B. A. Law—all well-known flyers.

Thirteen planes, in all, took the air in the attempt to assist in my rescue. All these planes circled around me, but there didn't seem to be anything they could do. Lieutenant Strickland evolved a plan whereby he would fly his small Thomas Morse airplane into the Houston Channel, land in the water, and then have my pilot cut me loose and allow me to drop into the water, where Lieutenant Strickland would pick me up. This plan might have worked, I do not know. I refused it, because I am deathly afraid of water.

Not everybody understood the cause of my predicament. Freddie Lund, flying by in another plane, had a barlow knife with which he planned to sever the small rope that kept my body dangling helplessly.

I quickly signaled with my hands the position of my parachute, and he then tossed the knife to me. I missed the blade by about two inches. Had I caught it, I would have tried to cut the rope around the top of the parachute pack. The only other plan Freddie could think of was to change planes. Lieutenant Lund felt an instructor's responsibility for a student and was determined to leave nothing undone to effect my rescue. He made the change, but in doing so he had no safety devices, such as ladders or ropes, and to add to the danger he was wearing cavalry boots.

I shall never forget the sudden silence that rushed about me when Tommy Thompson, piloting Freddie Lund, cut his motor and hollered to Clyde Pangborn, piloting our plane, that Freddie was going to change from his plane to ours. Tommy flew his plane only four feet from the one piloted by Clyde Pangborn and under it, so that Freddie, standing on the top wing of his plane, was able to jump to the lower wing of our plane. He then joined Captain Girton on the landing gear. Captain Girton, meanwhile, had continued to haul up on my rope and tie it to the landing gear. They combined in the hauling process, but their pooled strength still remained insufficient.

Then Lieutenant Lund changed seats with Clyde Pangborn, who, in turn, came down and began helping haul me up. With his help, the two men succeeded in lifting me to the top of the parachute bag, but because of the limited space on the clearance, with two men already standing on it, it was impossible to lift me to where I could also have found room to stand. The clearance was only eighteen inches between the wheels, and the parachute bag was three feet in circumference. I cannot say that I was frightened;

actual fright seemed to be out of my mind, which was bent solely on being rescued.

I could sense Freddie's exhaustion by the way the plane swayed and staggered as he piloted it. It seemed that the attempts to rescue me were to be futile, when, as if by inspiration, I hit upon a plan. I hollered up to Pangborn to put his foot down. He sat astride the spreader bar with one foot dangling while Captain Girton sat in the same manner on the other side. I caught hold of the toes of both shoes with my fingers and pulled myself up. When I was up high enough, they grasped me under the arms and cut the parachute loose.

Even in the midst of this precarious situation, I had to smile at an amusing incident connected with this final act of my rescue. Mr. Pangborn, in his effort to keep from dropping me, zealously caught me by the trousers and almost propelled me over the spreader bar and out across the cross wires which, of course, would have meant instant death. After I was on the spreader bar, they asked me if I could crawl up into the cockpit, but I found my strength unequal to this additional tax upon it, so Captain Girton and I hung onto the landing gear, while Clyde Pangborn returned to the cockpit and took over the controls from Freddie Lund, while Freddie crawled into the front.

We landed after forty-three minutes of the most trying ordeal any of us had ever experienced. Then, upon landing, another cause for excitement presented itself to us—we had only enough gas to last for three more minutes of flight!

More than one pilot in an aerial emergency has found that events move so swiftly that individual actions merge into a blur, and that little can be recalled of the sequence of incidents. One story that well illustrates this point concerns the case of Major Horace M. Hickam, a leading fighter pilot in the days when the "hottest" fighters still had fixed landing gear, a bi-plane configuration, and beautiful waxed surfaces.

During a swirling mock dogfight, Major Hickam collided with another fighter. As he related the incident later, there was little or no warning. The planes were "mixing it up a bit" in a mad scramble against each other, when suddenly ripping sounds came clearly over the roar of the engine, and Hickam's airplane staggered as though it had run into a wall.

Hickam stared briefly at his wings. The struts had snapped like matchsticks, and the wings were tearing into shreds of fabric and splintering wood. Then, one last screech of disintegrating supports, and one wing folded completely.

Momentarily, the fighter continued in level flight. Hickam moved swiftly to take advantage of the moment. Quickly he released his seat belt and prepared to jump. That was as far as he got. Without warning, the airplane jerked into a violent whipstall. The nose came up and then burst downward in a wicked slicing motion, and the airplane rushed in a vertical dive toward the earth.

Major Hickam hardly had time to notice this. What held every fiber of his attention was the tremendous stench of raw gasoline. The fuel tank had ruptured. Gasoline burst outward in a geyser and, slammed back by the wind, drenched Hickam's body. One thought crowded all others out of his mind. Fire! If the ship should start to burn, he would go up like a flaming torch.

Desperate, he kicked and fought his way clear of the wreckage. The wind wailed like a banshee, and Hickam winced inwardly every time he thought of the exhaust gases streaming back from the engine toward his gasoline-soaked clothes. The fighter vibrated and shook with the blows of the wind: for an instant Hickam was free.

Then a terrible crash as his body thudded into the tail section. Before he could even feel the pain, he knew he had struck the tail and caromed off into space. His next impression was that of floating peacefully to earth under his parachute.

The greatest dread the flier knows is fire. During World War I, as we have seen, men trapped in flaming airplanes had only two choices: to leap to their death or to stay with their aircraft and burn.

There are many incidents of men fighting for their lives in airplanes on fire. With the advent of the parachute, hundreds lived who otherwise would have faced the grim choice of the pilots of the Nieuports, Sopwith *Camels,* and Fokkers. Yet, not even fire and the option of the parachute can drive some men to abandon a blazing airplane. From the many moments in the history of aviation, I have drawn one incident that best represents the caliber of the men who flew our military aircraft back in the late 1920's.

Two men were involved: Lieutenant James T. Hutchinson, the pilot, and Paul Stanley, the observer, who performed the various functions of gunner, engineer, bombardier, and the duties of a combat crewman.

Hutchinson and Stanley had taken off in a bomber from McCook Field. They climbed to 8000 feet in a plane sagging with the weight of two thousand rounds of machine-gun ammunition, six heavy bombs, and several hundred gallons of gasoline. The wings and fuselage were fabric, and self-sealing fuel tanks were then a dream of the distant future. Any time one of the old planes staggered into the skies with this kind of sensitive and explosive load packed to its frame, it became in itself a flying bomb demanding the most exquisite care and attention.

They cruised at 8000 feet, holding course for a gunnery and bombing range. They never reached their destination. Without any warning, the engine erupted in a violent explosion. One moment they flew at cruising speed with everything working perfectly; in the next, the engine blew up. Hutchinson stared in disbelief as the thick firewall between his own body and the engine bulged toward him and burst. It didn't crack or fracture; it burst like an overripe melon thrown to the pavement from a great height. Yet this occupied Hutchinson's attention only for a moment.

Behind the bursting firewall came a dazzling, searing sheet of flame. The top cowling of the airplane seemed to lift upward slightly, hang a moment in air, and vanish in a flickering blur as the force of the explosion hurled it from the airplane.

In this elongated second of time, the flames splashed back into the cockpit. In horror, Hutchinson and Stanley endured the fire whipping throughout the confines of the cockpit and curling around their bodies. The entire nose of the airplane had vanished from sight. Flames spouted outward and, bent before the wind, knifed directly at them.

And the flames were riding the wind, sliding through the invisible airstream toward the gasoline tanks and the bombs!

"Jump! Jump for it!" Hutchinson cried above the bullwhip crackle of the flames.

In a blur of motion, Stanley flipped away his belt and threw his body from the cockpit. His body struck the edge of the wing and caromed sideways on the surface for a moment. For a long and impossible second he hung on the wing, and then he vanished from sight. His body was jerked from the propeller wash. Then he was clear, his body tumbling slowly end over end as he dropped toward the ground far below. White silk appeared, streamed out, and his body was jolted in the harness as the canopy deployed.

Behind him, Hutchinson had also scrambled from the cockpit. He climbed out to stand on the lower wing, his gloved hands gripping the brace wires. For a moment, out of the direct path of the flames, he stood there, as he said, "collecting my thoughts."

It was fortunate for the people of Dayton, below, that Hutchinson retained his presence of mind. For somehow his crippled engine continued to run; the propeller whirled and the yards vanished swiftly between the airplane and the city. Hutchinson, in "collecting his thoughts," remembered the homes and the people.

The airplane represented a potential catastrophe: the tanks

were still almost full; there were the bombs and the ammunition. In a single moment, the bomber could obliterate an entire block. . . .

Hutchinson started back into the flaming maw that was the cockpit. He reached the side of the fuselage. Searing heat beat at his body. And then he reached inside the cockpit, thrusting his arm into the flames! Wrapped in fire, his hand grasped the throttle and jerked it all the way back.

The engine snarl diminished, the nose dropped, and the bomber swung into a wide, gliding spiral.

Hutchinson tried to reach the switches to kill the engine entirely. He leaned deeper into the cockpit, but the flames slashed cruelly at his skin, and his lungs burned. Quickly he withdrew. Clothes smouldering, he crawled back on the wing and then let the wind pull him from the plane.

He pulled the ripcord. The chute blossomed out. For nearly a mile, the descending speed of the spiraling airplane was almost the same as the man in his parachute. Hutchinson stared in fascination as the flames crept back to envelop more of the bomber.

Then, slowly, the nose dropped to a steeper angle. The blazing plane eased into a dive and streaked like a meteor for the ground. A long pillar of flame and smoke marked the point of impact: an open field, away from any houses.

Hutchinson sighed in relief. He relaxed; for the first time in long and terrible minutes, he just—relaxed.

The silken angel brought him gently to earth.

CHAPTER 10

Test Jumpers

THE TEST JUMPER'S JOB is endlessly to experiment with parachutes, parachute subsystems, jumping techniques, and the development of survival equipment and procedures. Test jumpers perform a wide variety of missions, much of it a series of jumps that finally become repetitious. Few test jumps are ever made for records or as stunts. They are performed to help other men survive emergency situations.

The small group that worked with Major Hoffman at Mc-Cook Field developed new equipment—the standard parachute for military aircrews. Their jumps, as we have seen, were the first to test a new, free-falling, manually operated chute system.

It was common knowledge that pilots and test jumpers had leaped from airplanes at high altitudes and close to the ground. Nevertheless, most pilots still believed that jumps like these were not practicable in terms of everyday flying. The men had jumped under almost perfect conditions. The pilots argued that getting out of an airplane when it was burning or tumbling out of control was still an impossible task.

Again and again the pilots referred to the ideal conditions under which test jumps took place. They emphasized one example to prove their point about the weakness of parachutes —jumping from a plane that dove at high speed toward the earth.

In one particular incident, a diving fighter lost its wings. The pilot leaped from his cockpit and immediately pulled the ripcord. No one knows just how fast he was moving, but the speed proved great enough to snap the heavy harness webbing. The pilot's body streaked away from the canopy that fluttered uselessly behind him.

Other men died in high-speed chute openings. Sometimes the canopy panels tore loose. The chute folded in upon itself and "streamered"; it took the shape of a long, fluttering, and useless rag.

Sometimes the chutes split in half and collapsed. In several cases the opening shock was so great that the body of the chutist snapped up and into the canopy, snarling the man and his parachute and dooming the jumper. There were other cases in which the shock seemed to be so great that the canopy suffered friction burns and shredded apart in the air. The air at high speeds can resist movement like a brick wall. The parachute that opened suddenly was exposed to friction with the air. Sometimes it was so great that the heat of this friction weakened the canopy.

In some of these instances, the men survived despite the severe damage to the parachute. Some chutes withstood tremendous beatings. One pilot bailed out of a disintegrating fighter and immediately pulled his ripcord. The chute opened —and then the tumbling fuselage of the airplane smashed into the canopy!

The parachute wrapped around the fuselage and fell, whirling crazily, dragging the pilot to what seemed like certain death. Suddenly, the canopy split cleanly in two. It broke away from the wreckage, opened up again, and—despite being carved neatly in half—brought the man down safely.

Pilots were aware of these freak incidents but dismissed

Two Army jumpers are about to demonstrate the back pack chute, by sliding off the upper wing of this DH-4, in one of the more "exotic" departures from an airplane. (Air Force)

Perfect form and control is shown by an Army test jumper. The pilot chute is pulling the main canopy from the pack. (Air Force)

them as special cases. Rather, they believed that a man who bailed out from a plane at high altitude, especially at high speed, was as good as dead. Parachute engineers and technicians argued with them but agreed that opening the parachute immediately presented grave dangers.

In Chapter 5, we reviewed the characteristics of a body falling freely through the atmosphere. We saw that the key to the rate of fall is the terminal velocity of the man, the speed at which atmospheric resistance prevents his body from falling any faster. At low altitudes this amounts to a falling speed of about 120 miles per hour. At higher altitudes, where the air is thinner, a man falls at a greater rate of speed, but he is constantly slowing down. As he approaches the earth, his speed during the final several thousand feet of descent slows down to 120 miles per hour.

The arguments of aerodynamicists meant little to the pilots. Fine for the scientists to jiggle with their slide rules, they said, but the scientist sits behind a desk, and we're the ones who may have to jump for our lives.

The problem was how to prove the lack of danger in free fall.

One man stepped forward as a test subject. This volunteer was an Army enlisted man, Sergeant Randall Bose, assigned to the aviation section at Mitchel Field, Long Island, N.Y. Bose insisted that free fall did not present any undue dangers and, in fact, could be used to great advantage by pilots as a means of dropping rapidly into lower, safer air. As a veteran of twenty-five jumps, he was ready to test his convictions with a deliberate free fall.

Friends of Sergeant Bottriell had pleaded with him not to attempt a high-altitude jump, and Bose's friends were equally eloquent in trying to talk him out of what they also considered to be a suicidal experiment.

Bose would have none of it. He went out of an airplane 4500 feet over the airfield. For 1500 feet his body plummeted

Mechanic's overalls, sneakers, helmet and goggles—and Navy test parachutist C. A. M. Scott is ready to go off the wing. (U.S. Navy)

toward the earth as his friends watched, several of them convinced that he would never survive. One man shouted, "He's unconscious! He'll never come out of it!"

It seemed that the onlooker was right. The sergeant rolled over slowly as he fell. Then he began to swing into a loop, his feet first heading groundward and then starting to point toward the sky. Almost at the same moment, several men shouted. There! A flash of white!

The canopy streamed back, blossomed out into a wide circle of silk, and noise of the opening *crack!* of the parachute drifted down. Scarcely one minute later, as his friends rushed joyously toward him, Bose landed on the ground, grinning broadly.

Several days later, Bose repeated the jump. This time he fell freely for 1800 feet before he opened the parachute.

He went out of the airplane in the same manner and began his fall exactly as planned, in complete control of his body. Very quickly he hit terminal velocity and fell at a uniform rate. But then something went wrong.

Bose could not recall whether he was falling face down or face up. Yet he knew that something terrifying took place. He felt as if a great hand had seized him gently. Then the hand began to turn him around; it was a palpable physical force. Very quickly the sensation began to change. The gentle grip intensified—a great and invisible whirlpool in the sky. Instead of falling in the slow tumble that he expected, his body began to spin.

In seconds the normal world vanished. Bose whirled crazily, his body flashing around and around until it became a propellerlike blur. Panic welled up in his mind. He controlled it by sheer willpower. Not for a moment did he lose his head. He played it safe. He grabbed for the ripcord and with all his strength dragged out the D-ring.

"Just before I pulled the ripcord," he explained later, "things started to go black before my eyes. I was spinning very violently and feared that I might lose consciousness."

Corporal Garland Cain, U.S. Army test jumper, shows perfect form as he leans back from lower wing of biplane bomber. He barely clears the wing before his hand is ready to pull the D-ring. Note smaller, more compact size of parachute. (Air Force)

The opening parachute swirled crazily as it streamed from its pack. To the great relief of the frightened observers, the lines and the canopy unwound and snapped clean into the familiar shape of the normal parachute.

Disturbed by the unexpected action of Bose's falling body, Major Hoffman immediately began a series of tests to acquire exact information on the characteristics of the falling body. Using dummies of the shape, size, and weight of a man, he discovered that under normal atmospheric conditions and at low altitudes, the falling body would reach its terminal velocity about eight seconds after beginning its drop. The distance covered as the body rushed to its maximum falling speed was calculated as 1200 feet. Scientific observations showed the maximum speed at that moment was 118 miles per hour.

This posed a vexing problem. At 118 miles per hour a man did not get into trouble from just falling. Why, then, did Bose get into such a dangerous situation during his second jump?

Hoffman did not know the characteristics of the spin that sometimes results from an extended free fall. Specialists did not understand it until years later. Some form of imbalance; no one is certain even today. But whatever that imbalance or particular position of the body is, it is enough to whip the pilot into a violent flat spin as he falls.

This spin is a killer. Normally, the center of the spin is through the pelvic region. If the man falls on his stomach, the spin centers through the pelvis. If he falls on his back, the center of gravity for the spin shifts to his stomach area.

It took many years to determine for certain that the spin exerts tremendous force upon the body. First, the centrifugal force of the spin flings the blood and body fluids toward the outside of the spin. The jumper undergoes a serious and damaging fluid shift; the blood pools in his extremities and is kept by the force of the spin from circulating normally. Pretty soon the world begins to go red, becoming darker and darker.

Because circulation is impaired, less blood returns to the

A long, free drop through the skies, and no sensation of falling; the jumper is in perfect control, hand on the D-ring. (Air Force)

heart and therefore a reduced quantity of oxygen-rich blood leaves the heart. The eyes are most sensitive to this oxygen loss: the man begins to suffer dimming of vision. This is the period of seeing a bright red color, blood pooling in the eyes. Soon afterward, depending upon the severity and the duration of the spin, he becomes completely blind. He is still conscious, but his oxygen-starved eyes no longer function.

Seconds later, he begins to sink into a mental whirlpool. The continued force of the spin begins to reduce the flow of blood (and oxygen) to the brain. There is plenty of blood pooled at the brain, but the same thing happens here that happened to the eyes: with impaired circulation, the blood brings less oxygen to the brain. Suddenly a black cloud envelops the man, and he lapses into unconsciousness.

The body continues to increase the speed at which it spins! Whirling like a propeller, the jumper finally smashes into the ground.

This was the trap into which Bose fell. On the very point of blacking out, he yanked his ripcord to open his parachute. He was lucky. Others caught in the killer spin had opened their chutes in desperation, but the parachute came out wildly, because of the rotation, and twisted into an impossible snarl or wrapped around the body of the falling man to seal his doom.

No one was certain what caused the spin. Some men spun; others did not. In 1925, another Army sergeant tackled the "invisible killer."

At Selfridge Field in Michigan, Sergeant Steven Budreau bailed out of a bomber at 7000 feet. For 3500 feet he fell with perfect control of his senses. Men who watched from the ground could hardly believe their eyes when the parachute opened; according to all the information they possessed, Budreau should have been unconscious from the effects of his long free fall, his body dropping like a rocket.

Not only was Budreau conscious, he made meticulous observations of everything that happened during the jump. "I was perfectly conscious all the time. There was a curious, distorted sensation of great speed, but it was not disconcerting."

Pilots rejoiced over Budreau's jump, but it was still only a single jump. Three years later, several Navy parachutists planned a series of scientifically monitored free falls in order to determine, once and for all, whether or not a man could drop for thousands of feet and still remain master of his situation.

From the Navy's parachute training school, three enlisted

men—Crawford, Morgan, and Whitby—stepped forward as volunteers. On April 4, 1928, with hundreds of spectators watching, they started their jumps.

Five thousand feet above the ground, Crawford rose in his cockpit. He hesitated a moment, then crouched, and dove away from the airplane. For 2800 feet he fell toward the earth; then, silk blossomed forth.

Morgan went out at the same height and extended his free fall slightly, for a distance of 3000 feet. The two jumpers waxed enthusiastic about their drops. "It's as easy as falling downstairs," they laughed. "Your mind is as clear as a bell. There's a severe jolt when the canopy fills, but that's all!"

Then Whitby went out at 5100 feet. Let him tell about it.

Immediately, I started to tumble. I made two or three quick tumbling loops. I could see bits of the sky flashing between my boots; then the darker color of the earth.

My body seemed to be acted upon by a series of forces. The tumbling ceased abruptly, and I fell into a flat spin. Then I sensed that I was spiraling straight down, and the idea came to me that I might be able to kick myself free by moving my legs—as a pilot controls a spinning ship.

That seemed to work. I fell straight down, and the wind was whipping straight into my eyes.

Despite the rolling and turning that took place at different moments, there was a curious calm throughout the fall. Everything remained clear; to my own inward astonishment I found myself picking out the barracks where I lived from the scrambling of buildings.

There was a distinct sensation of speed, a whistling of wind in my ears which, after the first few seconds, became of an even pitch. My hearing, however, seemed to go, and my eyes seemed to cloud with water.

About this time, I swung helplessly into another loop; and so near did the ground seem that I decided to release the parachute at the peak of the next turn. I seemed to turn very slowly, and as my head swung down I saw the green grass on the field very plainly.

I decided not to wait any longer and grabbed the ripcord ring.

Whitby selected the most inopportune moment to deploy the chute. Apparently his body was at the worst possible angle and attitude when the canopy filled. It opened with a *crack!* so loud that Whitby reported that it sounded like a rifle going off right alongside his ear. People on the ground more than three miles away heard the sharp report, and the sudden stop proved so violent that, as the shroud lines extended and then suddenly retracted, Whitby whipped back upward completely into the canopy! Fortunately, he fell free again before the canopy folds could fold and snarl about his body, and he drifted safely to earth.

Whitby's record for the free fall was a distance of 4400 feet. On the ground, discussing the details of his jump with parachute technicians, he ridiculed the belief that falling through the air was, in itself, dangerous. "All this talk of infinite speed and loss of consciousness is bunk. It's possible to judge when you attain the region of terminal velocity by the varying intensity of the whistle in your ears. The first impression is one of acceleration. Then, one actually feels a slowing down. Thereafter, the speed perceptibly steadies, and the scream of air in one's ears maintains a monotonous steadiness."

From that day on, only the uninformed airman still believed that an extended free fall by itself could harm a man.

Whitby's jump for 4400 feet satisfied requirements for the late 1920's and early 1930's, but other men kept stretching out the distance of the free fall.

One of the greatest of all the jumpers—stunt man, engineer, technician, and test jumper—was Arthur H. Starnes, the same Art Starnes who pulled the famous "slide on the seat of his pants" at air fairs and circuses; the same Art Starnes, in fact, who once dove out the side of a *Cub* throttled down to 65 miles per hour—without a parachute and into a river 100 feet below!

In 1925, the same year that Budreau made his free fall of 3500 feet, Art Starnes first learned the magic of the long drop through the air. He jumped at 5000 feet and opened his chute a half mile below. This so exhilarated him that he kept increasing the length of his free falls.

In 1928, when the three Navy jumpers took the headlines for their free falls up to 4400 feet, Art Starnes was already far ahead of the military. The steel-nerved stunt man on a number

Not all test jumps start out well, but this one finished perfectly. This Army test jumper's chute tangled in tail of his plane. A second plane lowered a knife to Private Harold B. Osborne in the snagged chute; he cut himself free and came down safely with his reserve chute! Note his perfect control and form as he is dragged through the air. (Air Force)

of occasions jumped at 9000 feet, fell all the way to 1500 feet, and then opened his parachute. One-and-one-half-mile free falls were no novelty to this parachute artist!

In the 1930's, Starnes raised his sights. He went higher and higher and finally reached 18,500 feet before jumping. From a record-breaking 7500 feet for a free fall, Starnes extended the distance of his drops to several miles. His spectacular successes, marked by amazing presence of mind throughout his long falls through the air, inspired other jumpers to repeat his feats. Soon men fell for 10,000 feet and more. Their numbers increased, and the old fears of the long free fall began to fade away.

Even as Starnes and other men continued their jumps, fighting broke out among many nations of the world, not only on the ground but in the air as well. New fighters and bombers soared to heights once considered the private domain of research planes that struggled to 30,000 feet and higher above the earth.

In Spain, the airplanes of several nations were used by both sides fighting the Spanish Civil War. Warplanes of Germany, Russia, France, the United States, England, and other countries roared into battle. For the first year or two of the war, most of these airplanes were biplane fighters and old and slow bombers. Then new, faster types appeared.

The Russians poured in hundreds of sleek Mosca monoplane fighters. Barrel-shaped, the low-wing Moscas could fly at well over 270 miles per hour. They carried four heavy machine guns and took their pilots to well above 20,000 feet.

The "star" of the Spanish Civil War, however, was the German Messerschmitt Me-109B. The sleek German fighter could fly faster than 300 miles per hour and climb to more than 30,000 feet. Armed both with cannon and machine guns, it was the deadliest warplane used in Spain.

By 1937, a full-scale air war raged in China. To fight the

Five men went up in this single-engine biplane used for Navy test jumps; only the pilot was aboard when it landed. (U.S. Navy)

Japanese invaders, the Chinese asked for help from volunteers. These men, under the direction of General Claire Chennault, were banded together in the Foreign Legion of the Air. They flew Vultee V-111G dive bombers, a heavy single-engine, three-place raider. A main part of the bomber force used Martin B-10 bombers from the United States. The twin-engine airplanes flew many missions against the Japanese.

More than four hundred Russian fighters and bombers also fought in that war. The best Russian fighter was the same Mosca that had been sent to Spain.

Opposing the different planes of many nations, the Japanese

fought with a skilled, well-developed air force. They used hundreds of twin-engine bombers. Early in the fighting in China, their fighters were Kawasaki, Nakajima, and Mitsubishi biplanes. Then the Japanese moved in two new types: the Mitsubishi 96 and Nakajima 97 monoplane fighters. Despite their fixed landing gear, the Japanese planes could fly at about 300 miles per hour.

By 1939, the stage was set for the "new generation" of fighter planes. The Messerschmitt used in Spain had developed into the Me-109E, which flew at about 370 miles per hour. England produced the beautiful *Spitfire* and the sturdy *Hurricane*. From Japan there came the famous *Zero*. All of these new planes flew at speeds of 330 to 370 miles per hour.

It was a new kind of war in the air. Fighter pilots sometimes showed no hesitation in gunning down men as they drifted earthward, helpless in their parachutes.

In Spain, a young Loyalist pilot, a Spaniard named Luis Muñoz, shot down a Franco plane. The pilot bailed out as his fighter exploded into flames. Muñoz swung around in a wide circle as the parachute carried the Franco pilot down. And then Muñoz took careful aim and opened fire with his four machine guns. The fusillade of bullets tore the helpless flier to pieces and ripped the parachute into shreds. What Muñoz didn't know was that Franco forces on the ground had watched the whole thing and reported it to their headquarters.

A week later, the Loyalist forces lost one of their own pilots, who descended in a forced landing behind Franco lines.

The Falangists had not forgotten the man gunned down in his chute by Muñoz, and they reminded the Loyalist groups that their memory was good. The day after the Loyalist pilot landed in enemy territory, a Franco bomber flew over his home field. A large object fell from the bomber; a parachute blossomed out. When the Loyalist pilots opened the box, they found the body of their friend, his arms, legs, and head twisted and torn from the torso.

Such was the reaction of most pilots to the practice of gunning down men helpless in their chutes. Nevertheless, the practice continued. In the face of modern weapons and mass bombings, it seemed impossible to continue chivalry in the air.

Starnes, reading about Muñoz and others, hit upon an idea. Since a man *could* free fall, why not teach combat crewmen to do the same? In this fashion they could bail out from a stricken plane at great heights, fall freely through the air to only 2000 or 3000 feet above the ground, and then open their parachutes. In this manner they would prevent their helpless exposure during a long parachute descent.

Starnes had jumped from nearly four miles high. But to prove his point that a man could "go all the way," he would have to go even higher. He would have to jump from the very foot of the stratosphere—from 30,000 feet or above.

In the spring of 1940, he began preparing for his epochal leap. This meant careful exposure in decompression chambers to high altitude, practice and familiarization with equipment he would use during his drop, timers and an altimeter, and special clothing to compensate for the severe cold, which might be down to 60 degrees below zero. He wore his equipment and made five practice jumps from low altitude; after each jump he made minor modifications to his gear until he declared everything "ready to go."

Fully equipped, the 190-pound Starnes weighed nearly 260 pounds. He used a standard Irvin back pack with a 28-foot-diameter canopy as his main chute and a 24-foot chest pack as his emergency chute. To be certain that the extreme cold wouldn't foul the parachutes, he froze the assemblies (paying special attention to the ripcords) in the cold room of an ice cream company at temperatures down to 65 degrees below zero.

He carried a shortwave radio strapped tightly to his body, the microphone imbedded in a special face mask; as he fell, he would record his feelings and sensations. On his right forearm went a sensitive altimeter. There was a 16-mm. movie camera, externally mounted stopwatch, and other equipment. Then, to round it off, the doctors attached medical sensors to his body to obtain unprecedented medical data as Starnes plummeted from six miles high.

In event of an emergency with the parachutes, Starnes designed a special harness with which he could immediately jettison the heavy equipment and reduce his weight by some forty pounds.

On the day of the jump, a twin-engined Lockheed *Lodestar* with superchargers fought its way up to 30,800 feet, into the substratosphere. And then it was time for that fateful step *out*.

Starnes left the *Lodestar* in a clean flat dive, under control from the moment he went headfirst away from the airplane. At first he experienced a strange empty feeling; for a long time he had been exposed to the thundering roar of the two powerful engines and then, suddenly, the moment he left the *Lodestar* there came an abrupt and overwhelming quiet. Five or six seconds after leaving the airplane, Starnes was convinced he had reached terminal velocity.

He explained that the wind felt as though it were alive—not wild and violent, but tugging gently and persistently around his body as he fell. The air rushed past his ears much louder than he expected, a strange rumbling vibration. He yelled loudly several times, but heard nothing when he shouted.

Starnes did not try for any particular position. Instead he dropped from the sky in a slow and easy end-for-end fall that kept changing his body attitude and shifting the center of gravity of the fall. He was an experienced jumper, and the flipping of the horizon and sky did not bother him at all.

He had selected 2000 feet for the opening of his parachute, and as he dropped he compared his own visual impressions with the reading of the altimeter on his forearm. At 2000 feet he yanked the D-ring.

At that moment Starnes had been falling for 116.5 seconds. The chute deployed fully at 500 feet, giving Starnes a drop in free fall of 29,300 feet! Scientists estimated his highest speed at 230 miles per hour. After that, Starnes kept decelerating until his 260 pounds reached a terminal velocity near the ground of 130 miles per hour.

Because of his heavy weight, Starnes decided to add some protection as he drifted earthward. He pulled the ripcord of the second chute, floating down beneath both canopies. Two minutes later, he dropped to the ground.

At that moment Starnes knew that he had opened a door—a door to survival—for hundreds and perhaps thousands of men who would in the near future be fighting high over the earth, over the surface of much of the entire world.

And even Starnes' own jump soon was to be eclipsed. As World War II began, Major Boris Kharakhonoff of the Russian Army dropped away from an airplane within the stratosphere. It was the Soviet major's 599th jump.

Kharakhonoff left his airplane at a height of 40,813 feet, two miles higher than Starnes' record-breaking starting point. The Russian fell freely until only 2100 feet above the ground, where he pulled his ripcord and sailed gently to the earth.

The long free falls of men like Starnes and Kharakhonoff answered many questions about bailing out at extreme altitude and delaying opening of the parachute. It answered many questions—but not all.

A war was raging around the planet in 1943. Men were fighting eight miles and more above the earth. Fighters and bombers struggled into the thin, cruel air of the stratosphere. Sometimes at the touch of enemy bullets, sometimes because of equipment malfunction, the machines failed. In the terrible cold of these heights, strange things happened, and men were sometimes forced to abandon their craft. What would happen if a man had to bail out from an altitude of eight miles? What would happen if he opened his parachute immediately?

A man called Lovelace risked his life to find the answer to that question.

CHAPTER 11

Hell at 40,000 Feet

IT IS 1943. At 40,000 feet it is bitterly cold. A screaming wind bursts upward through the open bomb-bay doors of the B-17 *Fortress*, tears with ice-needle fingers at the clothes of the man standing at the edge of the bay looking down into the abyss.

Seventy degrees below zero, cold impossible to comprehend but terribly real and dangerous, severe enough to freeze a man's hand rock-hard within seconds.

There is another enemy: the cruel, thin air of this height. On the face of the man staring down at the featureless surface of the earth is an oxygen mask, its rubberized bladders alternately sucking empty and then puffing into a bloated bag, like lungs exposed nakedly to the air. Only that mask and its bladders lie between life and unconsciousness within ten to fifteen seconds should the mask fail, clog, freeze, or suffer even a minor leak.

The man is Lieutenant Colonel W. R. Lovelace of the Army Air Forces, and he is preparing to step out into the emptiness of the gaping bomb bays and attempt an unprecedented parachute descent to the earth far, far below. The oxygen equip-

ment worn by the colonel? Untried, untested, unproven at this
height, under the extreme conditions of terrible cold and rare-
fied air.

Colonel Lovelace is completely out of his element. He has no
business here. He has never made a parachute jump. He is a
surgeon with skilled hands who belongs in an operating room,
saving the lives of men in need of probing and cutting and
healing. And yet, here he is at 40,000 feet, prepared to make
a jump that has every chance of wresting his life from him.

Only one other man in the entire world has ever stepped
into the awesome emptiness of this height for a parachute
jump. But the Russian major who dropped away from his airplane departed the stratosphere as quickly as his falling body
would drag him down to denser, safer, warmer air; inside of
a minute and a half, the Soviet officer dropped free of the
perils of altitude, to be embraced by the thick ocean of air
closer to the earth.

Colonel Lovelace is going to attempt something that no man
has ever done. Most doctors are certain he will be dead long
before his feet ever touch the ground. Lovelace is going to
open his parachute immediately upon leaving the great
bomber!

It will take him twelve minutes to reach a level where he
can breathe without his vital oxygen bottle. There is the danger that the opening shock of the parachute may hammer
him senseless; the equipment may snap free; the hose-line may
fail—perhaps it will freeze. In 1943 engineers know precious
little about the effects of such severe cold and wind.

As far as Lovelace is concerned, it is imperative that he make
this jump. Pilots and their crews already are fighting in mor-
tal combat at this height. Can they survive a jump if they are
forced to bail out at this altitude? Will their equipment keep
them alive? The colonel believes that Air Force doctors should ·
hardly send men into combat, with aviation-medicine equipment, without knowing if that equipment will give the men

a chance to survive. There is only one way to find out. All it takes is a single step.

Colonel Lovelace takes a deep breath; he is ready for that step.

"Forty thousand feet seems much farther, looking straight down," he explained later, "than it does when you look out the side of a ship. It looks like a hell of a long ways. As we approached the altitude at which I wanted to leave the ship, things had been happening pretty fast and I was busy getting my equipment ready. You can't avoid a certain feeling of apprehension just before you jump, but the most careful preparations had been made and I didn't worry at all.

"I turned on my oxygen supply in the bottle zippered in my flying suit. Then I disconnected from the ship's supply and went on the bottle. I saw the oxygen pressure needle on my emergency equipment beginning to come around, and I knew I was all set.

"I stood there maybe forty-five seconds—that was the longest part of the jump! Then I went out feet first."

Lovelace falls through the bomb-bay opening. He goes out with the terrific roar of the wind and the engines pounding in his ears. There is a blur of metal and a flash of sky as his head passes the belly of the *Fortress,* then his body clears the bomber. The force of the airstream slaps him around, and he hurtles backward in mid-air. He sees the B-17 as he begins his fall, hears the now faint sound of its engines.

It takes only a second or so for his body to reach the limit of the static line. The line pulls taut, yanks the pilot chute from its folds. In an instant the full parachute comes out and snaps open.

The terrible jolt—a sudden, violent wrenching of every muscle, of every bone—jars him. He experiences immediate deceleration. In a fraction of a second he is brought from his high speed to a virtual halt. The force of the deceleration is the same as if he were hurled face first into a brick wall in the sky.

In that terrible moment before unconsciousness snatches him from pain, all the air is pounded from his lungs. There is a timeless moment in which he sees the leather glove and the silk glove beneath it fly away from his left hand. He sees it almost as if he were in a dream. Even as he is blacking out, his brain seeming to register things in slow motion, he realizes that he has suffered a blow of at least six times the force of gravity, perhaps even more. With all his equipment, the colonel in an instant has been exploded all the way to a weight of more than 1500 pounds! And that is all he knows as blackness envelops him.

His limbs sag. The next moment he hangs limp in the parachute harness, his left hand exposed to the brutal cold of eight-mile height. He falls, seemingly lifeless.

In the B-17, Dick Williams, the pilot, has racked the heavy bomber around as steeply as the thin air will permit. He comes around in a diving turn so the crewmen can spot the parachute and see how Colonel Lovelace is faring.

Someone shouts—but the sighting of the parachute is followed with a cry of dismay. "I think he killed himself!" one man calls.

It does look as if the colonel is dead, as he swings inertly in his harness. The parachute drops him toward the earth at the rate of forty feet per second. As he falls, his body swings limply from side to side, but in a wild and swooping arc of at least 45 degrees. It is a frightening sight for the men in the B-17, for at the end of each swing, the far side of the parachute canopy "laps in."

This is a partial collapse of the chute. The wild oscillations threaten to collapse the canopy at any instant and streamer the chute, and this is a sure warrant of death. Somehow, the chute holds each time.

Acutely aware that, even if he has survived the terrible

shock of the parachute opening and is still alive, Colonel Lovelace may be doomed to death at any moment, the B-17 crewmen follow him down, searching anxiously for any sign of life.

"Maybe he hit the plane as he went out," someone offers in the way of explanation, "or maybe the static line clipped him." Maybe. Maybe. They talk without any real knowledge, and they know this, even as they conjecture that the opening jerk of the parachute might have caused him to be struck about the head with some of his equipment, or even his own fist. Perhaps the oxygen line snapped, and he blacked out from lack of oxygen. Even, as they watch, he may be strangling to death.

Nine agonizing minutes pass. In this eternity of waiting, Lovelace drifts down from 40,200 feet to 22,000 feet, still more than four miles above the earth. At this height the earphones of the B-17 pilot crackle. Lovelace has been spotted by Boeing test pilots Bob Lamson and Cliff Dorman, who are circling at a lower altitude in an AT-6 trainer. The initial excitement of the sighting vanishes, for Lamson reports that there is still no sign of life. The colonel's body dangles helplessly in the oscillating parachute.

Somewhere during this part of the descent, Lovelace stirs to consciousness. He is still very far up. How high, he cannot tell. He looks "down a great distance" and then blackness once more engulfs him.

He drifts toward a layer of broken clouds, the AT-6 buzzing helplessly around his inert figure, Lamson and Dorman trying desperately in some way to help their friend. But they are only observers.

At 8000 feet Lovelace drops through a large hole in the clouds, and Lamson fairly screams into his mike. "He's *alive!* He's alive! I can see him moving!"

Lovelace is fighting his way back to consciousness. The sound of the AT-6 engine helps bring him to, and he raises his right hand in a feeble gesture of recognition.

The colonel is in bad shape, and he suffers a deep, burning pain. He is in shock, his body fighting the effects of hypoxia—oxygen starvation. He suffers from severe nausea, and his left hand is frozen almost solid.

Lamson notes with gratitude that just before Lovelace is about to hit the ground he slowly moves his legs. But the colonel's effort to prepare himself for the impact is futile. The earth rushes up at him, and he strikes the ground stiffly. Fortunately, he has fallen onto the flat expanse of a wheat field.

He topples helplessly to the ground, and the chute billows out. For several seconds it drags him along the ground. Luck stays with him, however, and the billowing silk collapses.

Right overhead is the AT-6, Lamson clawing around in a tight turn as he swings into the wind to land. Lovelace feebly waves a hand, and Lamson loses no time in following procedure. He radios the B-17 that Lovelace is alive, specifies his position, and asks for help. Then the AT-6 swings around sharply and slides to the ground.

Lamson leaps from the cockpit and runs to the colonel. Lovelace stirs feebly and cries, "God! I'm glad to see you!"

His face is the color of chalk. He can barely move his limbs. His left hand is a sickly, frozen white. The effects of his descent —nausea, shock, frozen hand, hypoxia—have taken a visible toll.

But all he says to Lamson is, "I'm all right. My hand hurts, and I feel just a little sick."

Lamson uses a portable oxygen bottle to feed pure oxygen to the colonel, who is trying to keep his frozen hand in the direct rays of the sun. He needs the oxygen badly. The rescue team arrives, and the doctor who checks over Lovelace orders him into the hospital immediately. There he is placed under oxygen. That evening the doctors permit him to drink some tea, but that is all.

By morning, however, Lovelace is on the upgrade. Later he recalls, "I didn't feel much like talking after I hit the ground.

Colonel W. R. Lovelace lands after his record-shattering jump from a B-17 in 1943. The Colonel opened his parachute at forty thousand feet; he suffered severe shock, frostbite, and oxygen starvation on the way down, but recovered completely.
(Air Force)

I noticed that I could form sentences all right, but some of the words—an average of one word per sentence—seemed to me to come out badly. I would attribute all that to lack of oxygen.

"They used to tell the men who might be in a spot where they had to make a high-altitude parachute jump to take a deep breath and hold it. But when you are bailing out there are a million things to think of, and I don't believe a jumper would ever be able to hold his breath. Even if he could, the deceleration would knock it out of his lungs."

Colonel Lovelace accomplished his perilous mission in one of the most amazing first jumps any man has ever made. Twenty years later, a parachute opening at 40,000 feet is still considered one of the most dangerous experiences any man can face, even with modern equipment and space-age medical research. From the lessons of Lovelace's jump, the Army Air Force was able to tell its fliers that, with emergency equipment, they could get out at high altitude and survive. But the Army recommended that the men ride their disabled planes down as far as they could do so in safety and, if they must get out, free fall as long as possible.

They're still telling them the same thing today.

CHAPTER **12**

The Parachute Goes to War:
The Bomber Crews

FEW PEOPLE who have not flown in the cockpits, or as crew members, of warplanes can conceive of the immensity of air battles. It is easy to talk of hundreds or even thousands of airplanes participating in the tremendous aerial missions of World War II, but it is something else again to understand and appreciate the size—of the forces involved or of the combat area.

Imagine a bomber stream in a massive assault, for example, against Berlin during the war. Just one day, one mission, out of the hundreds in which we fought. . . .

There are 2500 four-engine heavy bombers assigned to this one target. The sound of such a force is beyond imagining. In that stream of bombers there are 10,000 powerful engines, combining to make a thunder the like of which the world has never known before. Ten thousand engines, four to an airplane; the airplanes grouped into boxes in the sky: every box carefully planned so that each of the heavy bombers fits neatly into an over-all pattern.

So many bombers means a long stream. People on the

ground stare in awe at the spectacle before them: an armada in the heavens, a phalanx of thundering, vibrating, rumbling, roaring machines passing overhead. The sound comes first, even before the machines can be seen—sound that fills the heavens, that rolls and rumbles heavily across the land. Thunder in waves, wave after wave. Ten thousand propellers thrashing the air. Ten thousand exhaust stacks ejecting their blazing gases.

The bombers first appear in the distance as a blur. As minutes pass, the blur grows larger; it shimmers and gleams in the sunlight as metal shines dazzling bright. Then the blur resolves itself into individual shapes: gigantic, metal locusts. And then the first ranks pass directly overhead. Silver shapes with broad wings and long bodies, sound beating and thrashing mightily at the ground. The sound rolls and crashes and reverberates and echoes, becoming louder and louder and louder. When you hear sound like this the earth trembles; a man's belly feels the vibration, his ears and his eyes begin to hurt, and he himself begins to quiver through every muscle and every bone.

The great shapes pass overhead and begin to recede into the distance, but that is only the vanguard of the stream! Although the first wave is out of sight, an unbroken line continues to the point of origin, and there is nothing to be seen but a mass of great metal machines filling the sky—a stream a mile wide and a mile high and hundreds of miles long. For hours, the airplanes come.

Inside the swollen bellies of these giants there are bombs. Four tons to an airplane, 10,000 tons in all: 20,000,000 pounds of bombs! Bombs that spread out in flashing, devastating carpets to sprinkle armor-plated explosive death from the skies and transform cities into mushrooming spouts of flame and steel and smoke. And this is only the outside part of the armada.

Look inside the bombers. Within each of the four-engined

Armadas of bombers thunder into the skies over Germany. In every bomber stream of 2500 raiders there were more than 25,000 men who depended for their lives on their silken angels, should disaster befall their aircraft. (Air Force)

raiders there is a crew of eleven men. Twenty-seven thousand five hundred men within the sleek metal shapes; 27,500 men wearing oxygen masks and heated suits and gloves and steel flak helmets.

Nearly 33,000 heavy machine guns are within those bombers, some of them held in the gloved grip of men, others bolted within power-operated turrets. Millions of rounds of ammunition.

Accompanying these bombers is a force of escorting fighters. Fifteen hundred single- and twin-engine fighter planes: *Lightnings, Thunderbolts,* and *Mustangs* to protect the *Fortresses* and the *Liberators.* Each fighter also has guns—four or six or eight .50-caliber machine guns—in some airplanes there are also cannon.

This is the armada that invades the skies over the enemy land. All the bomber crews, all the fighter pilots—29,000 men strong.

To oppose them there will be from four to eight hundred German fighter planes, of all shapes and sizes. The German pilots will come thundering in to attack with Focke-Wulf FW-190, Messerschmitt Me-109G, and Heinkel He-113 single-engine fighters. These swift sharks will be armed with machine guns, cannon, rocket projectiles, and even bombs they will try to explode in the midst of the bomber formations. Twin-engine killers will roar against the American planes—Messerschmitt Me-110, Me-210, and Me-410 destroyers, each plane carrying from four to six cannon plus machine guns, their wings heavy with rocket tubes. German bombers turned into bomber interceptors—Junkers Ju-88, Heinkel He-117, Dornier Do-217, and others—will lumber into position to hurl rocket projectiles and cannon shells at the invading *Fortresses* and *Liberators.*

To support the operation, other men will fly diversionary missions. More heavy bombers, but also *Marauders* and *Mitchells* and *Havocs* and *Invaders.* There will be American and

"The flak was so thick you could get out
and walk on it." With its No. 2 engine afire,
a 15th Air Force Liberator punches its way
through murderous flak barrage. Many
times a bomber tore apart when hit
directly by flak, with little chance of its
crew bailing out. (Air Force)

British fighters—*Spitfires, Hurricanes, Typhoons* and *Tempests, Mosquitos, Whirlwinds*—and they will run high and run low with still more bombers: with *Beauforts* and *Lancasters* and with bulky, squat *Beaufighters,* each armed with six guns and four heavy cannon as well.

There will be support operations: men in cumbersome flying boats for search and patrol and rescue; men in small flying boats, in liaison planes, in all kinds of machines.

In this one theater of war, just this one theater in the air, men will fight and die. How many are there in this one arena of all the arenas which, during one day, will hear the waspish drone of engines, the cough of cannon, the whine of flaming, tumbling airplanes? Perhaps 50,000 men. Fifty thousand men in this one vast battle, so huge that its edges cannot be seen by any single observer, and every one of them will wear, or will carry, his own parachute.

It is strange to think of the enormity of these struggles in the heavens. More men in a single titanic engagement than there were in entire armies of past history. And yet there is no place to mark the sites where these men suffer, where they die, where their machines die with them. The atmosphere in an ocean, a great deep of gases never still, never silent. As quickly as a man dies the air is wiped clean. Nor does the battle itself remain still. It circles, it surges, it climbs and dives and swoops and zooms.

No one can visit the scenes of these great conflicts, as they might visit a cemetery of a hill, a ravine or a plain. There is left only a memory. But they say that, sometimes, a man who fought in that savage war below, within, and above the clouds returns to the land beneath the battle. If he closes his eyes and listens very carefully, it may come back to him: the muted thunder and the growling engines rising in sound, growing louder and louder, until the heavens themselves tremble and a fighter plunges down, burning, narrowly missing a bomber with ten or eleven frightened men who stare outward as the fighter pilot struggles at 500 miles per hour to hurl himself away from the flames. . . .

One huge, all-encompassing battle, and no man can see it all. But sometimes men write down what they see, men like Lieutenant Colonel Beirne Lay, Jr., who was in England in the late summer of 1943 when on only one of these missions (with a few hundred instead of a few thousand bombers) sixty giants fell from the skies.

It was not a battle of precision and neatness and order. The sky very quickly filled with debris, thousands and thousands of pieces. The airplanes shook and vibrated crazily, the men smelled the stink of burned powder, and there was a bedlam of wings with stars and black crosses, and the red and yellow noses of Focke-Wulfs and Messerschmitts. In Colonel Lay's words:

The Me-109s came in from twelve to two o'clock in pairs and in fours, and the main event was on. A shining silver object sailed past our right wing. I recognized it as a main exit door. Seconds later a dark object came hurtling through the formation, barely missing several props. It was a man, clasping his knees to his head, revolving like a diver in a triple somersault. I didn't see his chute open.

A B-17 turned gradually out of the formation to the right, maintaining altitude. In a split second, the B-17 completely disappeared in a brilliant explosion, from which the only remains were four small balls of fire, the fuel tanks, which were quickly consumed as they fell earthward.

Our airplane was endangered by hunks of debris. Emergency hatches, exit doors, prematurely opened parachutes, bodies, and assorted fragments of B-17s and Hun fighters breezed past us in the slipstream. I watched two fighters explode not far below, disappearing in sheets of orange flame, B-17s dropping out in every stage of distress, from engines on fire to control surfaces shot away, friendly and enemy parachutes floating down, and, on the green carpet far behind us, numerous funeral pyres of smoke from fallen fighters, marking our trail.

On we flew through the strewn wake of a desperate air battle, where disintegrating aircraft were commonplace and sixty chutes in the air at one time were hardly worth a second look. I watched a B-17 turn slowly out to the right with its cockpit a mass of flames. The copilot crawled out his window, held on with one hand, reached back for his chute, buckled it on, let go, and was whisked back into the horizontal stabilizer. I believe the impact killed him. His chute didn't open.

Ten minutes, twenty minutes, thirty minutes, and still no letup in the attacks. The fighters queued up like a breadline and let us have it. Each second of time had a cannon shell in it. The strain of being a clay duck in the wrong end of that aerial shooting gallery became almost intolerable as the minutes accumulated toward the first hour.

Our B-17 shook steadily with the fire of its .50s, and the air inside was heavy with smoke. It was cold in the cockpit, but when I looked across at our pilot—and a good one—sweat was pouring off his forehead and over his oxygen mask. He turned the controls over to me for a while. It was a blessed relief to concentrate on holding station in formation instead of watching those everlasting fighters boring in. It was possible to forget the fighters. Then the top-turret gunner's twin muzzles would pound away a foot above my head, giving an imitation of cannon shells exploding in the cockpit, while I gave an even better imitation of a man jumping six inches out of his seat.

A B-17 ahead of us, with its right Tokyo tanks on fire, dropped back to about 200 feet above our right wing and stayed there while seven of the crew bailed out successfully. Four went out the bomb bay and executed delayed jumps; one bailed from the nose, opened his chute prematurely, and nearly fouled the tail. Another went out the left-waist opening, delaying his chute opening for a safe interval. The tail gunner dropped out of his hatch, apparently pulling the ripcord before he was clear of the ship. His chute opened instantaneously, barely missing the tail, and jerked him so hard that both his shoes came off. He hung limply in

With two engines dead and left wing tank burning, a B-17 rolls crazily through the air. The first crew member to bail out is behind airplane with opening chute; second man is directly aft of the right wing. The entire crew bailed out —and just in time; the bomber exploded. This is one of the most remarkable combat photos ever made. (Air Force)

the harness, whereas the others had immediately showed some signs of life after their chutes opened, shifting around in the harness. The B-17 then dropped back in a medium spiral, and I did not see the pilots leave. I saw it just before it passed from view, several thousand feet below us, with its right wing a solid sheet of yellow flame. . . .

One B-17 dropped out on fire and put its wheels down while the crew bailed. Three Me-109s circled it closely but held their fire, apparently ensuring that no one stayed in the ship to try for home. I saw Hun fighters hold their fire even when being shot at by a B-17 from which the crew was bailing out.

Shorty Gordon, a gunner in 1943, brought home some other details of what it was like. He watched from a belly turret as a *Fortress* plummeted from a formation with four German fighters raking it with their guns and cannon. That heavy bomber went wild in the air. The pilot did things they said were impossible: he dropped the nose, picking up tremendous speed, and then swung up and up and finally over, rolling that giant airplane around in a huge and complete barrel roll. That B-17 got away from the fighters.

Another one did not. A Focke-Wulf came screaming in with a frontal attack, the German pilot slow-rolling as his wings and nose blazed with his weapons. "The Focke-Wulf was starting to roll over and go into the usual dive away from our formation when his wing hit the wing of a ship in the element below us," Gordon related. "The impact cut the wing off the fighter and knocked the wing off the *Fortress* just past its number four engine. The *Fort* started into a circle, then went into a tight spin. It broke in two right at the middle, and the ball turret went spinning down, looking like a baby's rattle. Then the wreckage exploded. . . ."

Nobody saw a single parachute.

Sometimes a man found need for a parachute that he never expected. The medical officer of the 381st Group (Heavy Bombardment), Eighth Air Force, recorded in a diary:

"Sometimes you don't need combat. On the ninth raid of the group, on 14 July 1943, a B-17 simply exploded en route to the target. The ship was over England when it tore to pieces in a blinding flash. Six men were killed instantly; the other four were blown into space and were able to pull their rip-cords."

Another medical diary recorded a bizarre incident of which the crews talked in wonder for many months.

"Just as the formation was reaching the Danish coast, a 20-mm. shell exploded in the cockpit of Lieutenant Winters' ship, and Lieutenant Winters was temporarily stunned or blinded by the flash. When he came to, the bombardier and navigator had already left the ship, the copilot was jumping, and one of the crew members gave him a farewell salute and jumped. The ship was in a steep, gliding turn, and there was a fire in the rear of the cockpit. Lieutenant Winters righted the ship, put on the autopilot, went back and put out the fire, and brought the ship safely back to England."

You can go back in history to the clashing of arms over Germany, over Italy and the Alps and Russia and anywhere else that men fought in the skies, and many of the stories are the same. Tales of heroism and of courage, of so many parachutes in the air sometimes that they became impossible to count. Not so many years before, a man bailing out at 25,000 feet performed a deed that seemed miraculous and suicidal, and to his friends and his associates he was, justifiably so, a hero.

But here, in one grand sweep of battle, men bailed out at 20,000 feet and higher, up to 30,000 feet, by the dozens, by the scores, and by the hundreds.

Sometimes, they did not bail out. Not all of them were able to free themselves. And sometimes a man chose not to use his parachute, when he could have done so. Take the case of a British sergeant: his name, R. H. Middleton. He flew a great *Stirling* bomber, an unusual occupation for a sergeant, a four-engine monster that for all the world looked like an over-size freight car with wings and a tail stuck on as an after-thought.

The *Stirling* staggered through the skies over Italy, torn and ripped and holed by German flak guns. The air over the target was alive with flying pieces of steel from a withering barrage of German anti-aircraft guns. But Middleton brought the great bomber over the target. He returned twice more, because the first runs left the bombardier unsatisfied.

It was bad enough at first, with the light flak guns that needled and pierced and shredded pieces from the *Stirling*. But on their third run over the target the heavy guns caught the range. Again and again, the blast waves rocked and battered at the heavy bomber. Steel fragments sang shrill cries of death as they tore into metal, ripped equipment, shattered Plexiglas, opened holes, raked steel.

Middleton fought desperately to keep his machine going and on an even keel. But finally he could do no more. A series of shells exploded below and to one side, and a great wave of air came up and slammed the bomber hard. The *Stirling* cried like a wounded animal and shot its wing high, shoving the other wing at the ground. Engines complaining, the bomber tumbled away from its precious lift and fell from its place in the sky.

In the cockpit Middleton stared grimly ahead, fighting at the controls. He could barely see. Then he heard a terrifying banshee scream. Flak had smashed the windscreen, and an icy hurricane howled into his face. The air whipped violently, the turbulence tugged and stabbed with hard fingers at him; he ignored it all and fought the dying machine that was his bomber. On the intercom, Middleton shouted for help in handling the massive bulk and weight of the wounded *Stirling*.

The men behind him were slashed, cut, bleeding. But despite his severe wounds, one man pushed down his pain and crawled forward on hands and knees. He grasped a metal stanchion in the cockpit and pulled himself to his feet. For a long moment he found himself frozen into place; he could not move. Middleton no longer had a face. A grotesque mask stared into the screaming wind.

A flak burst had shot Middleton's right eye completely

Riddled from nose to tail, a Liberator spurts flames through its fuselage, ready to explode. The crew is just starting to abandon their stricken airplane; note turret gunner fighting his way out of escape hatch just behind cockpit, where pilots are still at the controls. Every man was reported to have bailed out; the plane disintegrated into flaming chunks. (Air Force)

away. The skin was torn: a piece of bloody flesh fluttered wildly in the wind. The gunner stared at the open bone, exposed to the icy gale. . . .

Middleton never turned around. He wrestled with the controls, cursing the plunging, rocking bomber. The wounded gunner reached forward and grabbed the control column with his own hands; together, the gunner and Middleton hauled with all their combined strength on the column. The bomber shuddered; a long groaning cry sounded through the airplane, louder than the roar of the engines and the thunder of the wind. Metal banged somewhere in the fuselage, but they brought the airplane out of its dive, and they staggered back up to a higher altitude.

Middleton began the long, grueling fight home. While the other men attended their wounds, he stayed at the controls of the bomber, dragging the heavy airplane along rock walls, up into the mountains from the target in Italy, back to England. He scraped peaks in the dark, he peered into the howling wind, he fought and he pushed that bomber along.

And then, over the mountains, even his flesh and blood and will could stand no more. As though he had been struck a terrible blow, Middleton suddenly collapsed. His body lurched forward against the yoke, throwing the great airplane into a dive. The mountains rushed up.

A crewman staggered forward. He pulled the unconscious pilot from the controls and then hauled back with all his might on the control column, desperately throwing every ounce of his strength into this single deed. Slowly, like a wounded whale floundering at the edge of the ocean deeps, the *Stirling* lurched out of the dive.

The other men lifted Middleton from the pilot's seat. They themselves were in bad shape. One man nursed a raw wound in his leg, trying to stop the bleeding from a gaping cavity where a steel fragment had cleanly taken away a big chunk of flesh. The rear turret gunner bled from his head and his belly and his neck, and he coughed up blood.

Then the men discovered the true extent of Middleton's wounds. Not only was his face shattered, but he was cut and ripped in a dozen other places. Steel had sliced open his stomach; other fragments lodged within him. A chunk of flak had ripped open his right leg. Blood ran from an arm, where flak had flayed the skin to tatters.

Middleton regained consciousness and, it seemed, drew strength from some hidden well. He climbed back into the pilot's seat. Every time they passed over a city or an industrial area, the darkened earth spit flame and lanced shells upward at them. But they made it. They came over England, high in the air, the bomber droning its way home.

Over the English countryside, Middleton ordered his crew out of the airplane. Five men, three of them badly wounded, released their hatches and dropped away into the darkness. Their jumps were successful; the wounded received medical attention in time to live.

Two of Middleton's crew refused to go out. His crew—and his close friends. They stayed with the Old Man.

Middleton never tried to land that shattered wreck of a bomber in England. Badly wounded, half blind, his bomber loggy at the controls, the sergeant pilot refused to attempt a landing. There were people on the ground. They might be hurt if the *Stirling* got away from him.

So he flew over England, and in the night he flew out to the ocean on the other side. He flew away from home and country—and safety.

And the great, crippled *Stirling*, with its wounded and bleeding pilot, and the two men who refused to leave him, vanished forever in the sea. . . .

Colonel Budd J. Peaslee. An Old Man who led Mission 115 of the Eighth Air Force on October 14, 1943—Mission 115 in the record books, Black Thursday to every man who went along.

Two hundred and fifty-seven *Fortresses* crossed the German border on the way to Schweinfurt. One thousand four hundred German fighter airplanes, armed with guns, cannon, rockets, and aerial bombs, flown by skillful and courageous Luftwaffe pilots, waited for them.

On this day 600 men disappeared in the skies of Germany. Sixty of the big four-engine bombers never came home. Peaslee had some things to remember:

"I lean over, craning my neck to see clearly out the cockpit window. A few hundred feet in front of us a bomber has been hit by a rocket. I catch sight of it just as the right wing starts to fold upward. The fuselage opens like an eggshell, and a man dressed in a flying suit spins clear out in front. I see the pilots still at the controls, then the plane is swept with flame. The right wing breaks free, and with the two engines still spinning it drifts to the rear, flaming at the ragged end. The shattered mess disappears under our left wing, and the sky is clean again, but to me it is like a slow-motion movie scene."

An official report told briefly of one man whose life was spared by silken angel: "Exactly at 1357 hours, a rocket impacted with the wing root of B-17 Number 321, piloted by Lieutenant Clough. The wing blew off, a tremendous sheet of flame ripped out of the airplane, and it whipped into a very tight spin. One chute was seen to come out before the airplane exploded at 21,000 feet."

Another report left pilots white-faced and bitter: "On three different occasions, FW-190's swooped down and just over the parachutes of our men who had bailed out. They raced in close, propellers just clearing the chutes. The slipstream either scooped air out of the chutes or collapsed them, and on each occasion the chute and wearer plummeted to the ground."

Maybe a man named Art Starnes would smile in satisfaction

when he read reports, like this one from Staff Sergeant Peter Seniawsky, when he later told a story of how his B-17 was shot into disintegrating wreckage:

"We were hit everywhere and started to burn. The pilot told us to get out, and as fast as we could, we jumped. I delayed my jump intentionally from 20,000 feet down to 5000 feet . . . and while falling I watched the ground carefully, waiting until the layout of farm lands was clearly visible. Then I pulled the ring. After my chute opened I saw the B-17, burning heavily, disappear in level flight. I counted only three chutes."

Sometimes the battered, gashed, shattered B-17s brought the crews home—and then failed to land. On Mission 115 to Schweinfurt, forty men lived because of the packs they wore on their bodies. They had survived the worst of the flak and the Luftwaffe, but they could not land—and their parachutes brought them to ground safely.

A B-17 called the *Windy City Avenger* came lurching out of the sky to her British runway more a junk heap than a bomber. One elevator was shot to ribbons. As the *Fortress* slid down from altitude toward the field, the elevator "went completely berserk." Only 150 feet above the ground, the B-17 staggered crazily through the air. The terrified pilots fought her out of her wildness, struggled to 1000 feet. Then the pilot shouted into the intercom: "Let's get the hell outta here!" Seconds later the B-17 was empty, and all ten men came home safely.

At several fields, the runways disappeared beneath ground haze and a thick fog. Three *Fortresses* with thirty men droned helplessly in the soup, the pilots unable to locate the fields, not willing to hazard descent in complete blindness. They waited until the fuel was almost gone, and three pilots passed the word to their crews. Thirty men in the murk abandoned their airplanes, and thirty men came down to earth beneath white, silken canopies.

Sometimes bomber crews found themselves in terrifying situations from which it seemed they could not possibly escape with their lives, so suddenly did their airplanes burst into flames, stagger, and lurch violently in the air. Many bomber crewmen never wore their parachutes in flight. Instead, they wore their harness, with two strong metal rings at the chest front. If it became necessary to bail out, they would pick up a rolled chest pack, clip it swiftly to the rings, and jump.

There are cases where there was no time even to clip on the packs. More than one man grabbed a parachute in his hand and threw himself away from the flames roaring through his airplane. As he fell, he clipped the parachute to the harness, checked to see that it was secure, and then pulled the ripcord!

There was one British navigator who doubted that his story of survival would ever be accepted after the war. Over Germany during a night raid, an enemy flak burst struck squarely, and in one instant his bomber disintegrated in an explosion. One moment the airman sat inside the bomber; in the next he was falling through the air, without a parachute.

As he fell, he knew his death lay only seconds away. The greater darkness of the earth rushed up at him, and he closed his eyes for that final impact.

It came—tremendous stinging pains that suddenly vanished! And then, a white, savage pain through his leg, pounding against his body. He opened his eyes. He was alive!

When he struck the earth it was into the sloping branches of a high pine tree. Steadily decelerating, he battered his way down through the tree and plummeted into a deep snowdrift. German soldiers found him in the snow.

They threatened to shoot him if he did not tell where he had "hidden" his parachute. Only after investigating the wreck and checking out every detail of his story did the amazed Germans realize that he had, indeed, fallen several miles through the air without a parachute and survived only with a broken leg. The German authorities prepared a meticulous report of the affair, and in a group they signed the report to provide the navigator with proof of an "impossible" survival.

There have been times when a man in a burning or broken airplane was faced with the prospect of death because he had no parachute. Sometimes the chutes were shot into tatters or were caught in the flames of a dying bomber. Under these conditions, two men sometimes jumped with one parachute.

But there is not a single confirmed case of both of these men surviving their jumps of desperation. The shock of the opening parachute almost always ripped the man clinging to his friend away from the harness. (Remember the case of Tommy Walker and Dutch Wendt, two experienced jumpers, who failed to accomplish this feat under excellent conditions?)

But men faced with death will try anything. And other men, seeing their friends facing death, will do anything to help them. Men have tried to survive in this fashion with what they considered "sure-grip holds."

One man climbed on the back of his friend, locked his arms through the harness of the other, and scissored his legs in front of him. In this fashion they went out of their flaming bomber, almost glued to one another by muscle and sinew.

It did not work. The man wearing the harness cried out in helpless despair as the chute opened and he heard the *swish* of his friend's body falling away.

A matter of seconds took the life of one British gunner who almost performed what jumpers consider the impossible. Falling with a friend, clinging to his harness, he actually survived the opening shock of the parachute. He had tremendous strength, and when the canopy deployed, he was still clinging grimly to the harness of his fellow jumper.

They bailed out at 15,000 feet; this was the death sentence. About two or three thousand feet high, the strength of the gunner failed him; soundlessly, he slipped away to his death. Had the men bailed out at 10,000 feet, or delayed their jump for twenty or thirty seconds, both would have lived.

Two men survived "certain death" one night in England in bizarre escapes that were made even more fantastic when authorities later pieced together the details of the events.

A *Halifax* four-engine bomber took off with a two-ton load for a long night mission from Linton Airdrome. But only some twenty minutes later, fighting a storm, the *Halifax* plunged from the sky, its wings, body, and tail coated heavily with thick and glistening ice. It was only twelve miles from its base.

As the heavy airplane plummeted helplessly, a massive rock with all its ice load, the radioman-gunner, John Low, scrambled through a hatch in a desperate bid for life. Low was convinced that his move came too late, for he saw the ground rushing up at him as he cleared the bomber and yanked savagely on the ripcord.

It *was* too late, and the gunner was too low. But just as he realized that death would in another second claim him, the world vanished in a blinding flash. Directly beneath his falling body, the *Halifax* crashed. The fuel tanks and bomb load exploded, and the blast hurled Low's body several hundred feet into the sky, simultaneously tearing the parachute from the pack which had not yet had the chance to open.

Burned, in shock, and severely injured, Low was dropped roughly by his parachute on the roof of a building. Not only did he survive his ordeal—he was the only survivor—but he married the nurse who helped return him to good health!

Astonishing as was Low's miraculous escape, authorities were dumfounded when they confirmed another incident that took place only twenty minutes after Low's bomber exploded beneath him.

Another *Halifax,* carrying twelve 500-pound bombs, also fell from the sky with a heavy coating of ice. The time was almost an hour after takeoff, an hour of struggling through storms. The pilot had enough time to shout at his crew to bail out. A gunner, J. H. Waugh, wasted no time in obeying; he dove through his escape hatch and pulled the D-ring. The canopy streamed out and deployed low over the ground.

Waugh stared in horror as the bomber smashed into the ground directly beneath him and exploded. The blast of super-heated air sent him spinning skyward in a violent gyrating maneuver that hurled him up about six or seven hundred feet. And then the canopy collapsed!

Waugh realized he had met his end. Just as quickly as this realization came to him, the canopy opened again. Waugh dropped to the ground—unharmed.

It is impossible, of course, to select just one incident from the many concerning the bomber crews who flew and fought during World War II. But the temptation for the author to pick what he, personally, considers the "most outstanding" of all the case histories can be overwhelming. This is my own selection.

They say that miracles can take place in the sky; perhaps by miracle they mean an event that has the odds so greatly against it that they become astronomical. A British four-engine bomber on a night mission over Germany took a direct flak burst. As has happened more times than pilots like to recall, there came no warning. Flak was light until that moment, and then a heavy shell tore upward from the ground, exploded within the bomber, and in a fiery blast tore the great airplane to shreds.

Two men survived that blast—survived long enough to be hurled away from the remnants of what had been an airplane. One man had worn his parachute in the airplane, and for this he was grateful as the night air swallowed him and he fell toward the earth.

The second crewman did not have a parachute. His escape from instant death within the bomber left him with cold comfort, for he was now falling to certain death without any means of survival.

Neither man knew that his body fell through the air only scant feet away from the other.

The man without a parachute plunged toward the earth, helpless. He was high enough, with a strange and astonishing clarity of vision, to see the earth in bright moonlight. Suddenly, he struck something in midair!

Desperately, instinctively, wildly, he flailed out with his arms. There—his fingers grasped something! The air slammed out of his chest, but he hung with superhuman strength to whatever it was he had clutched. Only then, as his mind reeled in astonishment, did he realize he was hanging with desperate strength to the legs of his fellow crewman.

With the odds millions and millions to one, the two men had fallen closely together from their airplane. Never did they separate by more than a few yards.

About a mile above the ground, the crewman wearing the parachute, who was slightly lower, pulled his ripcord. The canopy boomed open, swinging the man around in a great curving arc and, at the top of the swing, almost to a horizontal position.

At this split second, before the man in the parachute began his swing back the other way, his fellow crewman fell onto his legs, striking when his friend's body was almost horizontal, the canopy far to the side. His instinctive grab for whatever it was he had crashed into gave him an excellent grip, and he hung on, all the way to the ground. Both men sustained injuries when they struck the earth but they couldn't have cared less!

CHAPTER 13

The Parachute Goes to War:
The Fighter Pilots

HE WAS TYPICAL of the breed of fighter pilots early in World War II—young, skilled and daring, aggressive and ready to tackle anything. His name was Yeager, Charles E. Yeager. At the moment he was on a practice flight in the United States, at the controls of a long-nosed *Airacobra* single-engine fighter. The subject of his delighted attention was a four-engine *Liberator* bomber cruising cross-country, fair game to any young fighter pilot. Yeager could not pass up the opportunity to make a series of mock attacks against the lumbering bomber. He made several runs from different angles against the other airplane and pulled up in a towering zoom. High above the other airplane, he rolled over onto his back, tucked the nose under, and plummeted in a screaming power dive.

Steeper and steeper until the Allison engine in the P-39 vibrated with the increasing revolutions. The fighter streaked earthward, and Yeager grinned from sheer exultation at the power and speed at his fingertips.

The grin vanished as the *Airacobra* exploded. No warning, not a sign of trouble—just a terrifying blast and then a sheet of flame whipping from under the seat into the cockpit. The fighter has two doors, one on each side, and even as Yeager saw the flame and winced from the explosion one of the doors vanished in the airstream.

Yeager moved in a blur of speed to save his life. He was on fire, diving almost vertically for the ground. Less than a mile away, the earth leaped up toward him. He released his harness and tried to struggle clear, but the wind clamped him tightly within the cockpit. Fingers of wind poked in, gripped his oxygen mask and helmet, and ripped them away. Desperate, Yeager rolled himself into a ball and then kicked his way out with his powerful legs.

His body tumbled wildly as he whirled around in the turbulent air. He caught a glimpse of the *Airacobra* going in, smoke pouring in a long dirty smear from the fighter. And then he was on his back, earth and sky gyrating crazily. The D-ring—in his hand; he pulled swiftly. The opening of the canopy at so great a speed jerked his body around as though he were a rag doll. In that same instant the force of the blow slammed him with a great fist, and he felt blackness enveloping him.

Yeager regained consciousness in a hospital bed. His back felt as if someone had slammed a sledge hammer into his spinal column, but he grinned when the doctors told him that he was on his way to complete recovery.

This experience was only the beginning for Yeager. In 1944 he was back in a fighter, this time strapped into the seat of a swift and agile P-51 *Mustang* in Europe, flying escort for B-17s on a long-range mission to pound Berlin. That day he flamed an Me-109 and came home with a scalp to paint on the side of his *Mustang*.

The next day the Luftwaffe got even. A swarm of FW-190s came diving out of the sun, and they hit the *Mustang* formation with all the force of a full broadside. Cannon shells tore Yeager's P-51 to pieces. One moment he was flying in a beautiful fighter; the next, the *Mustang* was disintegrating. The engine was in flames, the elevators were shot away, and then the oxygen system exploded and probed the cockpit with brilliant fingers of flame.

Twenty thousand feet over Europe, Yeager got the canopy free and jumped for his life, releasing his belt and diving wildly over the side. He did not know at the time that the staccato rain of explosive shells had rammed pieces of metal into both feet; neither did he realize that one hand had been severely cut and was bleeding badly.

Yeager dropped more than 15,000 feet in a long free fall, knowing that what other men had done he could safely do as well. Less than a mile up, he pulled the ripcord.

On the ground, he moved swiftly and furtively: Yeager didn't believe in giving up. He escaped from the Germans and made it all the way back to England, thus becoming one of the very few American pilots shot down who escaped and were permitted to return to combat in the same theater of war.

Yeager went back with a vengeance. On his first "return mission," he blew a German bomber into blazing fragments. Some days later, he came home to be pounded on the back and congratulated by his cheering wingmen; over Germany Yeager had cut five single-engine German fighters into wreckage. They were confirmed kills.

On November 6, 1944, the pilot who had twice saved his life by bailing out of burning fighters achieved a new kind of fame. In his propeller-driven *Mustang*, Yeager dove at full speed against a Messerschmitt Me-262 jet fighter. He watched the jet plow into the ground at high speed, becoming a single rolling ball of fire.

Two weeks later, in a furious dogfight, he shot down four Focke-Wulf FW-190 fighters. Again all the kills were confirmed. By war's end he had sixty-four missions, eleven air-to-air kills.

Charles Yeager's combat record is almost unknown to millions of Americans who know his name well, for this is the same Chuck Yeager who, on October 14, 1947, became the first man ever to fly faster than the speed of sound, in the old Bell XS-1. The same man, several years later, took the X-1A to another record of 1650 miles per hour and then tumbled crazily out of control for more than 50,000 feet.

Things seemed to come in twos for Yeager. Twice he saved his life by jumping, and twice he held the record as the fastest man in the world.

Tens of thousands of fighter pilots engaged in aerial combat during World War II, and several thousand of these men (no one has compiled a really accurate total, and the total never will be known) jumped for their lives from their crippled or uncontrollable aircraft. Any jump from a fighter plane in combat is a story unto itself. The odds are, of course, that many of them will after a while fall into a pattern, since the circumstances are so often the same.

Yet there were unusual jumps, as in the case of Lieutenant Vernon A. Boehle, an Eighth Air Force fighter pilot in Europe. After a bitter dogfight over Germany, during which Boehle had to draw every ounce of performance from his husky *Thunderbolt* fighter, the pilot cruised at 19,000 feet on a course back to England. During that battle the *Thunderbolt* had been damaged, and damaged more than the pilot realized.

Boehle cruised steadily. The air remained comfortably smooth. And then the engine fell out!

"The Jug began to vibrate and the whole plane shook like a toy," Boehle related. "Then the engine dropped off the mounts and out of the plane. I saw her drop. My plane did a couple of tight loops, then started into a flat spin. I tried to transmit a distress signal, but the radio was dead. I got ready to bail out and climbed out of the cockpit, but I just flopped around on the wing. I thought I would bounce off, but the centrifugal force kept me glued to the wing and I believe I would have

A dramatic sequence of death escaped by seconds: the Thunderbolt riddled Focke-Wulf FW-190 at point-blank range. In the first two pictures (left column, reading down), German pilot tries to escape and fails. In third picture (bottom left), wing near fuselage is burning, and pilot has jettisoned his canopy. In fourth picture (top right), pilot is fighting his way clear of the cockpit. Pictures five and six (two bottom right photos) show the pilot free of the airplane. (Air Force)

stayed there all the way down if I hadn't kicked myself off with my feet."

Other pilots were trapped by their airplanes. It wasn't always possible to break free, and some went all the way with their stricken fighters.

General Adolf Galland, chief of the Luftwaffe's fighter divisions in World War II, has pointed out that the pilots of the Messerschmitt Me-109 fighters that fought over the English Channel preferred not to jump in an emergency when their plane was going down. This was in contradiction to the practice of most pilots, who chose jumping rather than landing a crippled airplane on the water, which often was rough and as unyielding as concrete.

As Galland explained it, the German pilots preferred to ditch. They felt this choice was much better than bailing out and parachuting into water. A man often lost his survival equipment; the parachute snarled his body; he had to get rid of his harness while soaking wet, being dragged down, encumbered by his Mae West—to mention only a few of the problems.

The single-engine Messerschmitt usually remained afloat for forty to sixty seconds, and this gave the pilot more than enough time to scramble out on the wing, inflate his one-man dinghy (life raft), climb in, and push away from the sinking fighter.

But when a plane burned or was uncontrollable, there was always the matter of *how* to get out. Many pilots dove over the side. Some of them went for the wing and slid off. The British began the practice of jettisoning the canopy and rolling the fighter over on its back; then a pilot released his belt and simply fell away from the airplane. Despite the fears of some pilots of striking a part of the cockpit, this became one of the most widely used procedures of getting out of a fighter.

Many pilots, including the Germans, used a different technique. They would release the canopy, unfasten their belts, and then ram the stick forward. The fighter pitched down

Chuck Yeager is an outstanding Air Force test pilot. Twice he saved his life by bailing out of crippled fighter planes; twice he held speed records as the fastest man in the world. (Air Force)

violently, and the sudden movement literally hurled the pilot out of the cockpit and into the air. Many Marine pilots flying big *Corsair* fighters in the Pacific employed this method. They felt that it was the fastest and surest means of getting out quickly, a point to consider, especially at low altitude.

But of all the pilots whose airplanes inspired unusual bailout procedures, none could match that of the Fifteenth Air Force pilots who flew the big twin-engined, twin-boomed P-38 *Lightnings* in the Mediterranean Theater. The Fifteenth lost a number of pilots trying to bail out of crippled P-38s, and the men studied carefully different ways and means of escaping with their lives. Then, one P-38 burned in a dogfight. The other pilots saw the big *Lightning* pull up in a steady climb, power reduced, until it hung in the air in a stall. Even as it approached the stall, the canopy came back, the pilot scrambled out atop his cockpit, and then jumped *between* the booms! Unorthodox, but it worked.

General Galland personally knew the problems of getting out of a crippled fighter. A superb pilot, Galland was not only a commander but one of the Luftwaffe's crack aces.

On one mission, Galland's Messerschmitt caught a heavy crossfire from enemy guns; armor-piercing and incendiary bullets tore the plane into a flaming wreck.

The Me-109 has a hinged canopy that swings up and to the side for normal operation. When his fighter began to fall apart into flaming chunks, Galland found that he could not get the canopy free; it trapped him inside, with powerful metal shackles, imprisoning him within a cockpit that grew hotter by the second and showed the first tongues of flame coming back from the engine. Galland hurled his body again and again at the canopy, trying to pitch himself free of the Messerschmitt.

His parachute, instead of acting as a means of preserving his life, became a trap. He broke free of the canopy and began his jump, but the chute pack snagged the edge of the cockpit roof!

The P-38 Lightning *fighters of World War II were deadly. Four of
America's ten top aces flew the* Lightning, *and two of these—Dick
Bong and Tommy McGuire—were the two highest-scoring aces of
the war. Their pilots developed a technique of abandoning the P-38
when hit by pulling up into a stall—and jumping between the twin
booms!* (Air Force)

184 🛩 THE SILKEN ANGELS

The German ace found himself trapped, half in and half out of the airplane as it headed earthward. The wind howled back at several hundred miles per hour, pouring the flames into Galland's face and body. Frantically he struggled to get free. He wrapped his arm around the fuselage antenna mast and pulled in a frenzy.

The world seemed to dissolve. Galland to this day doesn't know how he broke loose, but abruptly the roar faded and cold air replaced the searing flames. He found himself plunging freely through the air, whirling and tumbling as he dropped freely toward the earth. Sobbing for breath, he hauled on the D-ring, to begin a safe and controlled descent beneath his canopy.

Heinz Knoke, another German ace, nearly met his end before the heavy machine guns of some wild-flying *Thunderbolts*. Caught in a wild melee over Germany, Knoke made the mistake of underestimating the performance of the heavy American fighters. One P-47 locked on to his tail and poured the concentrated fire of eight .50-caliber guns into Knoke's Messerschmitt Me-109G, in a deadly sawing motion.

In a moment the fighter burst into flames. Knoke jettisoned his canopy, released his safety belt, everything happening with a ring of familiarity, because this was not the first time that he had gone out of a burning Messerschmitt.

Before he had the chance to pop the stick forward and catapult himself clear, the wind pounced into the open cockpit and jerked him violently from his seat.

Knoke was stunned to realize that quite suddenly he was trapped. He dangled partially in and partially out of the falling fighter plane. The parachute was snagged on a projection within the cockpit; Knoke had his left leg inside, and the right was out in the wind on the fuselage.

Then the Me-109G rolled slowly over on her back, tucked in her nose, and broke free in a thundering power dive for the earth. Knoke still was unable to get clear, but the wind became a great knife blade tearing and slashing at him.

The wind with tremendous force pulled at his body, trying to snatch him free and whirl him away. But his left leg remained clamped in the cockpit, and the wind whipping violently in the small space tore and twisted it. Knoke felt a stab of pain; his knee was completely out of joint.

Flames raced back along the fuselage. Knoke could hardly breathe; he was smothered in pain. He knew that he was shouting but could not do anything about it. A flash of crimson rushed before his eyes; blood poured from his nose in the terrible wind. Somehow, with the strength of a doomed man, he managed to get his right leg back into the cockpit. He kicked madly at the control stick. The fighter whirled crazily through the air, and in the next instant his body sailed through a great wall of flames, and he knew only that something struck his head with great force.

It was the tail of the airplane, slamming against his head as he pitched aft. His body scraped along the fuselage, and the metal tore open the edge of his parachute pack. The German pilot was still unconscious when the canopy blossomed. Knoke regained his senses in awe, for he was floating gently toward the earth, and the D-ring was still firmly in place!

But of all the men who were ever trapped in a crippled, falling fighter plane, none met the situation better—or better equipped—than Wing Commander Douglas Bader of the Royal Air Force, one of the greatest names in flying.

Douglas Bader flew in combat without any legs. Several years before the war began, a low-altitude crash pinned him in wreckage that crushed both legs. The doctors amputated. Other men would have been resigned to the end of their flying lives and would have accepted their fate as invalids. Bader accepted nothing save a grim resolve to persevere. And he did. He remained in the RAF, he learned to walk on artificial legs, to run, and then to drive. One day he climbed back into a fighter plane. In a mock dogfight he flew circles around other pilots. Bader was not only a man who could fly with artificial legs but also one of the greatest pilots in England.

In the summer of 1941, over the Pas de Calais, German fighters caught his *Spitfire* in a neat scissors and shot the lithe fighter airplane into bits. Bader felt the *Spitfire* start to shake wildly, and then "pieces began flying off my crate." The nose shot suddenly downward; the airplane pitched violently, out of control. Bader looked back and his eyes widened. Where there had been a tail, now remained only twisted metal.

Bader discovered quickly that getting out of a tumbling, uncontrollable fighter was bad enough for any man. Doing it with artificial legs seemed impossible.

As he released the canopy, the shattered *Spitfire* rammed its nose down into a vertical dive, attained terrifying speed, and whirled into a tight spin. Fighting the wind, battling the centrifugal force of the spin, the indomitable Bader clawed his way up from his seat with his powerful arms. In the wind of several hundred miles per hour, he managed to get one artificial leg outside the cockpit.

But the other leg was wedged tightly within the cockpit! Bader tugged and strained with the desperation of a man who knows he is going to die—and quickly—unless he can tear himself free. Pulling frantically, Bader hurled himself away. Suddenly, the *Spitfire* vanished below him.

His artificial leg went with the airplane!

With only his left artificial leg to cushion the shock, he dropped to the ground with a stunning, pain-stabbing crash. The impact was so great that it rammed the artificial leg brutally against his chest. The Germans at the hospital to which he was rushed reported him as being in a "terrible state."

Later, German mechanics recovered the badly damaged artificial right leg from the wreckage of the *Spitfire* and did their best to straighten the limb out. The British pilot shouted for joy when the Germans handed him his leg. Immediately he tried to walk. He did, too.

A British fighter pilot streaked low in his *Spitfire*, a wingman holding hard to him slightly behind and to the right, as both planes poured cannon shells at German shore installations in a hair-raising low-level strafing mission. Behind them they left a trail of exploding fuel tanks and vehicles; then the cannon shells chewed into a coastal oil tanker and deep red flames mushroomed high over the shore, directly in front of the two planes.

The wingman managed to skid out of the way, but his leader plunged directly into the holocaust. As the *Spitfire* burst clear of the fire, the flak found the range, and a withering barrage of bullets and shells smashed against and into the fighter plane. The *Spitfire* plunged into the water in a geyser of flame, water, and smoke.

Back in England, the second pilot reported on landing that he had seen the other airplane explode with terrifying impact, disintegrating into "a thousand bloody flaming pieces." They listed the pilot as dead; who could survive that?

The "dead" pilot did.

He was only forty feet over the water when the flak barrage tore into his fighter. He recalled that he had come in fast and hard, four cannon hammering away, when the world exploded. One moment he looked through his gunsight, and in the very next instant there were flames and overwhelming noise.

That was all. The next thing the pilot knew his body was hurtling through the air, the airplane had vanished, and his parachute was just starting to deploy. At the very same moment, he smacked with brain-jarring impact into the water. As the parachute began to collapse over him he caught a glimpse of the shattered *Spitfire*—a long trail of disintegrating wreckage—smash into the sea next to him. Immediately, he forgot about the *Spitfire*, because he was going under water and the chute was fouling him. He struggled to fight clear of the canopy.

The shore lay several hundred yards away, and as he surfaced, spitting water and gasping for breath, his limbs weak from the exertion, he struck out for land. No German moved to help; they were convinced the pilot was dead. He swam for a while, fighting the weight of his clothes. Steadily he sank lower and lower into the water, cursing the fates that had let him escape an impossible situation and now seemed certain to drown him.

His body went lower and lower—and suddenly the pilot's mouth opened wide in astonishment. The water was only four feet deep!

He walked the rest of the way to shore.

One British fighter pilot very quickly discovered that his normal world had vanished before a burst of German cannon shells. As he dove after a Messerschmitt, another fighter whipped around on his tail and poured shells into his *Spitfire*. In less time than it takes to tell, the exploding shells tore the fighter airplane cleanly in two and set it aflame.

The pilot hauled back on the sliding canopy over his head. It snapped back about nine inches—and stuck. Desperately the pilot struggled to break free. He squeezed his head and shoulders through and then had to stop, clamped tightly in place. Helpless to move, he realized he was going to die.

Two hundred feet above the English Channel, in a what's-the-use gesture he pulled the ripcord anyway. The next thing he knew he was lying face down in water, along a beach!

At the very moment he had pulled the ripcord, the fighter had exploded. As he stood in the cockpit, already free of his seat belt, the partially spilled chute caught the force of the blast wave and filled almost instantly with air. A split second after the canopy boomed taut, whipping his body almost to

A German bomber gunner shot the left wing completely off this Hawker Hurricane; the pilot jumped as the fighter flipped wildly. Note pilot and opening parachute at top. This is one of the great combat photos of World War II. (Royal Air Force)

a halt, he struck the water. He rose shakily to his feet; except for some bruises, there wasn't a mark on his body.

A German pilot bailed out of his Me-109G in almost a vertical power dive as his fighter accelerated rapidly, its controls shot away. He hit the air at more than 500 miles per hour, and almost immediately—still falling at about 400 miles per hour—he hauled away in terror on the ripcord.

The impact of the opening parachute struck him with savage force. The blow proved so great that it snapped two of the body harness belts! Instead of deploying fully, the canopy writhed and then collapsed after its first instant of tautness. With a half-open parachute and fluttering silk behind him, the pilot plunged earthward. Just off the shore—no more than a dozen feet from hard earth—he crashed into the sea. That saved his life. His rescuers dragged him from the water. With several broken ribs, the German was spitting blood and cursing furiously.

A U.S. Marine pilot, Lieutenant Gilbert Percy, did the German one better by showing incredible presence of mind. Over the Pacific, Japanese fighters chewed up Percy's airplane. The controls were shot away, the airplane was burning, and the Marine bled from wounds inflicted in both legs and one arm by 20-mm. cannon shells. At 380 miles per hour, he fought his way clear of the uncontrollable airplane, only 2000 feet over the ocean.

As Percy tumbled violently through the air, his parachute snarled his body—and then streamered, a long and useless fluttering rag behind him. Not for a moment did this man panic. He achieved a remarkable balance of his body, kept his legs together, and used his hands to cup his groin and his face.

Falling for nearly a half mile, he plunged at 100 miles per hour into the water. The shattering impact sprained both his ankles and fractured his pelvis, adding to the pain and shock of his wounds.

With unbelievable strength, Percy managed to clear himself of his harness. He then swam for three hours until he dragged his battered and bleeding body onto a reef! Friendly natives rescued him the next morning.

One British fighter pilot cannot understand to this day how he ever survived his jump away from a diving, flaming airplane. He dove clear of the airplane, but the great speed built up in the dive' caused the airblast to strike his body a severe physical blow, pounding him unconscious. That was all he remembered about leaving his fighter: a murderous jolt over every inch of his body.

When he regained his senses, he discovered that he was falling through the air head first; a terrible pain running along one leg was so violent that he cried out in agony. And he knew, also, that he was going to die, because when he felt along his body the parachute harness no longer was there.

In the past he had wondered what it would be like to fall to death in this manner. Now he knew. With the strange calm and detachment that comes to a man under circumstances such as these, he tried to take stock of the sensations of his experience. Then, through the pain and the wind whistling by his ears, he heard a constant rippling and crackling sound.

But from what? He strained his neck to look past his body at the sky, and—there was his parachute! The canopy had been split down the middle, and the strange crackling and rippling sounds came from the panels flapping crazily through the air. But how? How could he be with the parachute when he had no harness? His mind spun: his leg . . . the pain . . . he looked again, disbelieving.

A single nylon shroud line was wrapped around his leg in a perfect tension knot, pulled taut—painfully taut—against his limb, secured by the weight of his own body. And in this fashion, with a split, flapping parachute, he fell out of the sky.

He struck the ground so hard that the impact pounded him senseless, dislocated his shoulders, wrenched his neck badly, gave him a terrific bump on the head, and broke several bones. Six months later, he walked normally.

Sergeant Dave Borthwick, an Australian fighter pilot, was shot nearly to ribbons by German fighters in North Africa. Borthwick's P-40E *Kittyhawk* began to disintegrate in the air as it burned, and the pilot struggled in the cockpit with both legs severely wounded.

The *Kittyhawk* streaked low over the desert at 400 miles per hour, while Borthwick struggled wildly to get clear of his fighter. The wind hammered him back in, trapping him halfway out of the cockpit. Finally, he began to inch his way free, looking in fear as the desert rose up to meet the plunging airplane. To hell with it. He yanked the D-ring, and the world went crazy.

The sergeant remembered hearing the booming *crack!* of the opening canopy and, less than one second later, feeling knives of pain stabbing through his legs. The second sensation was the impact of his wounded legs against the desert. In just that instant, the chute opened and he banged into the ground. Strangely enough, his wounds helped him to survive. His legs were so weak that they never resisted the impact and folded under him like rubber, cushioning the fall and sending his body tumbling over and over in the sand, absorbing the fierce blow of hitting the ground.

Lieutenant Dudley Davis of the Royal Air Force survived an amazingly similar near-death incident in 1940. Enemy ground fire chopped his airplane to shreds as he raced fifty feet over the ground in a strafing attack. Abruptly the fighter exploded into a long comet of fire. Davis had to get out immediately or be burned alive.

But he waited. With the flames sweeping into the cockpit, he waited until he was only six feet off the water. Wincing from the fire against his body, he jerked the bomb release in the cockpit and sent a bomb beneath the airplane's belly rifling toward a warship.

Then, and not until then, did Davis pull frantically back on the control stick. As the airplane zoomed, Davis released the cockpit hatch and scrambled out, his body completely immersed in the sheet of fire from the engine. For a fraction of a second his feet were on the wing as he yanked the ripcord.

Fifty feet over the ground, the parachute streamed out and filled. The blossoming canopy swept him backward; his body thudded painfully against the tail; in almost the same instant he pounded into the ground.

Davis' parachute never had time to drop. It deployed and yanked the pilot from his airplane. Davis swung downward in a wide arc and hit the ground. He was burned, bruised from the impact, but he rose to his feet and walked away.

Colonel Chesley Peterson, an Army Air Forces pilot in Europe during the war, began his combat career as an Eagle Squadron pilot with the Royal Air Force. During this duty, the rear gunner of a Junkers Ju-88 bomber shot his *Spitfire* into wreckage, and Peterson bailed out. He landed in the English Channel, floated in his dinghy until a crash boat picked him up, and returned to combat. But this was only his first visit to the Channel.

Later in the war, flying a P-47 *Thunderbolt* with the U.S. fighter forces, he took a terrific beating from the cannon fire of a Focke-Wulf. The *Thunderbolt* began to come apart in a dozen places, and at 1000 feet Peterson bailed out, clearing the fighter cleanly.

The parachute deployed behind him—but failed to open! It fluttered uselessly in the air as he fell to what seemed like certain death in the Channel.

Peterson smashed face first into the water. A British rescue flying boat landed almost immediately, hoping to recover the colonel's body before it sank beneath the surface. The crew was stunned to find Peterson alive.

He was in great shock, suffering lacerations and bruises almost over his entire body, and he was blind. Peterson regained his sight, recovered from his injuries, and went back into combat.

He ended the war with nine kills in air-to-air fighting.

It took the pilot of a *Typhoon* fighter to go Colonel Peterson one better. The British pilot hedgehopped over the ground at treetop level while he blasted away with cannon fire at German ground defenses. German flak was good, and their aim on this occasion proved to be both accurate and overwhelming.

The pilot saw tracers converging in a stream toward him and then "the whole blasted world blew up in my face. That's all there was to it: flying one moment, and then nothing but an explosion."

The stunned pilot found himself, a fraction of a second later, sailing through the air, still strapped to his seat but without an airplane! The *Typhoon* had literally disintegrated into flying bits and pieces all around him, leaving him unscathed in the very center of the explosion.

Too low to release the belt and pull his ripcord, he had only a fleeting instant in which to realize death would come when he struck the ground at better than 200 miles per hour.

The German gunners watched the incredible sight of the pilot, strapped tightly to his seat, disappear in an enormous running cloud of spraying water and—mud.

Mud that was soft and yielding, thick but wet; mud that acted as a perfect shock absorber that steadily decelerated the seat and the pilot. When he came to a stop, the spray and mud showering down upon him, the pilot didn't have so much as a bruise on his body.

These are bizarre escapes. Yet some of them reflect the measure of the men who were involved. It would be unfair to leave the impression that luck always prevailed. There were other men who deliberately risked the odds, and lost.

Flying Officer Tuff was an Australian pilot flying *Typhoon* fighters from England against German defenses on the European mainland. After one sweep at low level, from which everyone emerged, the group re-formed. They climbed for altitude as they cruised home over the Channel.

But one airplane had been hit. Tuff watched his flight leader sink toward the sea in a crippled *Typhoon*. Just over the surface, the pilot eased back on the stick and ditched the heavy airplane cleanly into the water.

While the other planes circled high overhead, Tuff dove to low altitude, sweeping around in a tight banked turn. He called to the other men that the flight leader had made it away from his sinking airplane. Tuff could see the dinghy low in the water.

The sea was bitter and cold. The nearest help was ninety miles away. Tuff knew this; he knew also that the pilot must have been wounded, that he might have been hurt in the ditching. Tuff knew also that his flight leader wore contact lenses, that his eyes would be two deep sockets of pain from the salt and the water.

"I'm going down to help him!" With that message Tuff rolled the *Typhoon* onto its back and dropped away. His parachute opened, and Tuff drifted into the sea to help his injured friend. The other pilots called frantically for help, then had to run for home before their fuel ran out.

They never saw either of the two men again.

The early days of the fighting against the Japanese in World War II were a far cry from the massive steamroller offensives we hurled at the enemy during the second half of the war. The opening phase of the war in the Pacific was a desperate struggle in outmoded airplanes against a force that hurled overwhelming odds against a pitifully small force of defenders.

One of the men best representing the bitter struggle in 1941 and early 1942 is Gregory R. Board, an Australian fighter pilot who flew ancient Brewster *Buffalo* fighters against Japanese *Zeros* and waves of Mitsubishi twin-engine bombers.

Board took off from Ipoh, on the Asiatic mainland, as part of a force of eleven *Buffalos*. More than fifty Japanese fighters and bombers droned steadily toward their targets as the Australian pilots struggled for altitude. The *Buffalos* dragged themselves to 25,000 feet, providing the small force with an advantage it needed desperately against the *Zeros*, altitude—altitude from which to dive and build up as much speed as possible in the opening wedge of the attack.

The Japanese formations slid into view far below the *Buffalos*. Eleven barrel-shaped fighters rolled over and plunged earthward, throttles all the way forward, in near-vertical dives, the pilots squeezing every last bit of speed from the airplanes, all the way down to 12,000 feet.

Board dove without a waver in his line of flight as the *Zeros* whipped around in sharp climbing turns to meet the attack. One Mitsubishi mushroomed in size within Board's sights, and a short, accurate burst turned the *Zero* into a whirling ball of fire. It made Board's third kill in the young war.

He had little opportunity to think about that third kill or anything else except the *Zeros* still in the air. The agile Japanese fighters came screeching around on his tail. Board threw the *Buffalo* all over the sky, but a *Zero* hung on like a leech. And right behind the *Zero* came a *Buffalo*, then a *Zero*, and another *Buffalo*—five fighters in a macabre, twisting, and weaving pursuit through the skies.

The Japanese pilot behind Board was good, and he had an airplane far superior to the *Buffalo*. Cannon shells and machine-gun bullets began to hack Board's fighter into pieces of flying metal. Gregory Board was—and is—a superb flier, but he was caught in a box from which he couldn't readily escape.

The instrument panel blew apart in his face, and he could hear and feel bullets and cannon shells crashing into the armor plate behind his back, thudding against his body. He stared at his wings as the *Zero* shot much of the top surfacing of the wings clean off the airplane. And then the *Buffalo* began to shred. Board flicked the fighter into a half roll as he flung the

Old, slow, and poorly armed—that was the Brewster Buffalo in which Gregory Board fought Japanese Zero fighters in Malaya after Pearl Harbor. Board flew superbly in his outmatched Buffalo against the Japanese and flamed several enemy planes. When his fighter went to pieces and exploded into flames, Board rolled over and dropped free, bailing out into the jungle. The next morning he was back in the air in another Buffalo. (U.S. Navy)

Greg Board today; the Flying Fortress behind the pilot is one which Board and the author flew to England in 1961. A fighter, bomber, seaplane, transport, airlines, and helicopter pilot (and some other ratings besides), Board is president of Aero Associates, Inc. of Tucson, Arizona. (Martin Caidin Archives)

airplane in a vertical dive toward the earth. The speed built up immediately; the engine howled, pieces flew off the airplane, and the *Zero* clung grimly to his tail, still chopping out deadly short bursts.

By now Board's fuel tanks were aflame. Acrid fumes swirled in the cockpit; his remaining ammunition exploded within the wings and the nose. Board hauled back suddenly on the stick and tramped rudder; the *Buffalo* clawed up and around into a cloud. Board figured he would come out of the cloud in a wide turn and still go after the *Zero*. But he was surrounded by flames, and the heat within the cockpit had become unbearable.

He rolled over on his back, jettisoned the canopy, released his belt, and dropped clear of the blazing wreck.

Board delayed in opening his parachute. He had seen more than one pilot riddled as he drifted down. So he fell until he could make out individual trees in the jungle below him and then pulled the ring. For the first time on this wild day, things went in his favor. The canopy snarled in a high tree, the tree groaned and bent all the way over toward the ground, and Board just stepped out!

He had only a pistol—no survival equipment, no water. The jungle was so thick it took him an hour to struggle a distance of 400 yards along a creek. Two days later he came face to face with natives. They took him out of the jungle and back to his base, and the following day he cut another *Zero* fighter out of the skies.

Not all pilots were as expert as Greg Board, and sometimes they paid dearly for their inexperience. Marine Lieutenant Sam S. Logan, twenty-two years old, dove to the assistance of a New Zealand P-40 being shot up by a *Zero*. Even as he gunned the *Zero*, the Japanese pilot's wingman shot Logan's plane into fragments. As his fighter came apart beneath him, Logan bailed out at 20,000 feet. He pulled the chute open.

This was a mistake that proved to be costly. The *Zero* pilot who had flamed his airplane now selected Logan as a personal target.

Logan drifted helplessly in the parachute as the Mitsubishi came around in wide, lazy circles. The Japanese pilot was in no hurry; he came in, aimed carefully, and then cut loose with his guns and cannon. Fortunately for the Marine, the Japanese pilot proved to be a poor shot. He cut some holes in the parachute, but not a single bullet or shell touched the descending flier.

Logan's tormentor showed his growing anger. On his next wide pass, he came boring straight in at the Marine, the guns and cannon silent but his propeller growing larger and larger with each second. He was going to ram Logan! The *Zero* slid in closer and closer, the propeller whirling away like a gigantic scythe. At the last moment, Logan managed to jerk his body upward. The propeller blades passed inches beneath his body but did not touch him.

On the next pass, the Marine again tried to jerk his body out of the way. He saved his life but not his skin. The propeller chopped off part of his right foot and sliced away the heel of his left foot. Streaming blood and in agony, Logan had no strength left to try to evade the *Zero* any longer. He watched the enemy fighter boring in for a third time.

As he waited to die, a New Zealand P-40 plunged like a bullet from high above in a vertical dive, six guns pouring tracers at the *Zero*. The Japanese flick-rolled out of the way and ran for home. The New Zealand pilot passed up a sure kill to remain with Logan, circling him protectively until the Marine dropped into the sea. Summoning all his strength, Logan inflated his life vest, applied tourniquets to his legs, and was still conscious when a rescue plane fished him out of the ocean.

The silken angel that pilots wore as a back, seat, or chest pack was not always sufficient to insure survival. In the Aleutians, Alaska, or the Scandinavian countries like Norway, pilots often had to bail out into deadly cold—blizzards, ice, snow, and other Arcticlike conditions. Without special protection in the form of training and survival equipment, a man could not hope to survive; he would quickly succumb to the cold and winds, unless he had the means of protecting himself.

Into the survival kits for flying in these regions went the equipment that enables a man to survive the worst of the north. A kit contained medical supplies to meet all emergency purposes, such as cleaning wounds, setting splints on broken limbs, and providing the protection necessary to keep an injured man from being crippled; signaling devices, including mirrors which the pilot could use to reflect the sun; and a booklet telling the pilot how to stamp out messages in the snow or use rocks and brush to write coded signs to be read by planes that might fly over.

The pilot had either a folding shotgun or rifle—the stock folded neatly against the barrel, into a compact package, and could be easily pulled out into the complete rifle shape. He had fishing gear, snare lines to trap animals, and other equipment for hunting. He had emergency rations, a frying pan, incendiary pellets, and matches in waterproof packs for starting fires and cooking. A knife could be lashed to a long stick for a spear. The parachute itself was invaluable. The shroud lines could be cut for fishing, snares, binding splints, or other purposes. The panels could be cut for emergency clothing, as a windbreak, as door panels for crude shelters or igloos, as a net for small animals, or as a pack to carry food and supplies.

With knowledge of how to use this equipment, a man could survive the worst of blizzards and cold. Pilots went through survival training that, when the chips were down and a man was lost, enabled him to survive under what most men considered "lethal" conditions.

The kits were modified to meet different needs of different geographical regions, but they all carried the basic elements of medicine, weapons, and equipment for finding food in the immediate countryside. As important as any other item were the small pamphlets that described what kind of roots and plants a man could eat to survive, when normally he would never even think of grubbing for his food.

In the southwest Pacific, the survival kits had to be modified to meet the conditions encountered in the ocean and jungle regions. Built around the "basic" survival kit, these included protection against insects, snakes, poisonous lizards, and other jungle hazards.

But no matter what the part of the world, the kits—contained as part of the parachute packs, or worn separately on the body—proved to be the best friends pilots ever had.

Lieutenant Leon Crane bailed out over the northern Arctic wilderness. His parachute dropped him into snow so deep that he knew he faced a tremendous struggle for survival. For the next eighty-four days Crane fought his battle, a vicious fight that meant living through howling blizzards and temperatures that plummeted to more than 40 degrees below zero. With what the kit provided him, he eked food from the countryside. Finally, nearly three months after bailing out, he stumbled into a small, isolated town.

The parachute proved its role as the silken angel in yet other ways, especially to men on the ground who were desperately in need of assistance. Doctors and rescue specialists often jumped into remote areas to provide help for ailing or injured men. Representative of the specialist who was both doctor and rescuer was Captain Harve W. Jourdan, who went out of a plane at night in country completely unknown to him, to the hunting and trapping camp of Fish Lake in the Yukon, and saved the life of a dying man.

One captain, a flight surgeon, bailed out at night some two hundred miles from his base, after another plane spotted wreckage on a frozen lake. When the flight surgeon reached the wreckage after running across the ice, he found the pilot dead and a dog guarding the body. For the next four days the doctor and the dog huddled together, sharing their body warmth as well as rations and water. The temperature dropped to 30 degrees below zero. Sled dog teams finally rescued them.

Saving fighter pilots who bailed out often involved intricate teamwork on the part of many people and entire organizations, as in the case of Lieutenant Jim Hinkle. This Air Force pilot felt his *Mustang* reel sickeningly through the air over Osaka, Japan, in July of 1945, as a flak burst smashed into the fighter. The airplane reeled over and tumbled. Immediately Hinkle hit the radio switch and called out, "I'm hit and burning. . . . I have to bail!"

At once his wingman, Captain Jack Folsom, called to him not to bail out. Hinkle had righted the airplane despite the flames. "Keep it in a glide as long as you can," Folsom radioed to Hinkle. "Try and get offshore over the water. We'll fly cover for you." Hinkle did his best, braving the flames as long as he could.

The blazing *Mustang* eased over the coastline and staggered another three miles out to sea. Then Hinkle could take the fire no longer. He jettisoned the canopy and dove clear of the fighter, drifting beneath his parachute into the sea.

As he climbed into his dinghy, with Japan only three miles away, a B-17 *Dumbo* (rescue plane) cruised overhead at 500 feet in wide, protective circles. Much higher was a B-29 *Super Dumbo*. Other planes streaked in low over the water, dropping smoke markers on the sea for identification.

Hinkle noted the activity. A small aerial fleet was operating just to protect him, in the teeth of powerful Japanese defenses. Suddenly, a few feet away from his life raft, a huge submarine broke the surface. Hinkle could hardly believe his eyes as American sailors rushed to the deck, hustled the pilot into the conning tower and down into the submarine, and seconds later began a crash dive, right under the noses of the Japanese!

Ready to complete a round trip: Navy team rescues Army pilot shot down by Japanese fighters in the Pacific. Man in water is Navy crewman who went out in raft to pick up downed pilot. (U.S. Navy)

In a similar incident, Lieutenant Colonel Charles Taylor abandoned his burning *Mustang* eight miles from the Japanese coastline. The Navy moved in swiftly. Less than five minutes after he dropped into the water beneath his chute, Taylor was in a submarine and on his way to safety.

Picking up men from under the very muzzle of Japanese guns became routine, but routine always fraught with danger. There were enough proven incidents of Japanese brutality to lead many pilots and crewmen to prefer death to capture by the Japanese. One incident alone will suffice to illustrate the basis of their fear.

At Puerto Princesa in Palawan, in December of 1944, Japanese soldiers herded 150 American prisoners into concrete bunkers seventy-five feet long. When all the Americans, most of them pilots, were within the bunkers, the guards hurled buckets of gasoline in after them from both sides. Other guards ran to the entrances and then heaved in flaming torches.

The tunnels exploded in blinding flames. Screaming in agony, burning alive, the Americans dashed out, and were either mowed down with machine guns or stabbed with bayonets by laughing Japanese.

Forty Americans hurled themselves over the edge of a nearby fifty-foot cliff. Off shore, Japanese troops in boats poured a withering rifle fire into their flaming bodies. Many of the men who doused the flames by immersion in water were dragged back to shore, their skin blistered from head to foot. As a reward for survival, the Japanese buried most of them alive and slowly tortured the rest.

For reasons such as these, our men would go to any lengths to avoid capture.

Sergeant Jack Cannon, gunner on a B-29 attacking Japan, described his most harrowing mission:

"Bombing Myazaki airfield near the south tip of Kyushu, we got a direct hit through the front compartment. It must have

In a setting of cathedral-like majesty, a great B-29 burns high over Japan. Moments later, over Kobe, the stricken bomber plunged earthward in flames. (Air Force)

killed or seriously wounded the copilot, navigator, and bombardier. We started down like an anvil, but the pilot got control. He sounded calm on the interphone. We asked if we should bail out. He said, 'Hell, no, everything's going to be all right. Ride her down and prepare to ditch.'

"I sat tight until the flames swept back and my blister (Plexiglas gun-sighting blister) started to melt. Then I went to the waist. The pilot gave the okay, and the men started bailing. We went lower and lower, and I could see the fleets of sampans flashing past us as we cleared the coast. Then I went out, the last to jump. Almost at the second the chute opened, it seemed, I hit the water."

A *Super Dumbo* thundered overhead, dropping a huge emergency lifeboat (including engine and fuel supply) by parachute to Cannon. Then the big B-29 turned hard and dropped its nose. The roar of engines at full throttle echoed across the water as the pilot raced at wavetop height toward the fleet of Japanese sampans rushing to capture the downed gunner.

The B-29 crew raked the sampans with a devastating fire from its .50-caliber machine guns. Four of the sampans were torn to pieces and sank, while the others reversed course and got out of the way as fast as they could move.

A rescue submarine came in under maximum speed. Cannon stared in dismay as a Japanese bomber roared in against the submarine and dropped a stick of bombs. The aim was bad, which is understandable, since the Japanese pilot was stunned to see the great B-29 diving after him with gun turrets blazing. The Japanese plane fled, the B-29 circled like a great protective bird, and Cannon scrambled aboard the submarine. As the men hustled down the conning tower, one sailor turned for a moment toward Japan and thumbed his nose at the whole Japanese empire.

CHAPTER **14**

Trap in the Sky

DESPITE THE MANY THOUSANDS of successful bailouts and escapes from crippled airplanes during World War II, there remained a disconcerting number of men who failed to clear their machines and were dragged to their death. The problem increased in severity with the higher performance of airplanes. At the beginning of the war, speeds of 350 miles per hour in level flight in airplanes such as the Curtiss P-40 *Tomahawk,* Mitsubishi *Zero,* Hawker *Hurricane,* Messerschmitt Me-109E, and others were considered excellent. By the last year of the war, speeds rose to well over 400 miles per hour flying straight and true. Germany's Messerschmitt Me-109G, Heinkel He-113, Focke-Wulf FW-190; Britain's latest *Spitfire* models, *Typhoons, Tempests,* and *Mosquitos;* and the *Lightnings, Thunderbolts, Mustangs,* and *Corsairs* of the United States all exceeded 400 miles per hour in level flight.

Much more significant was the fact that these swift and heavy fighter airplanes accelerated within seconds to great diving speeds: well over 500 miles per hour.

At this speed it proved almost impossible for a man to fight his way out of an airplane. It happened sometimes, but the odds were against it. If the airplane was designed with a canopy that jettisoned (blew away from the fighter) the chances of getting out were better. But many fighters had sliding canopies, and pilots in these machines knew their chances for survival at very great speeds were small.

The wind at 400 miles per hour is more than five times as powerful as a full-blown hurricane. Air at this speed has the force of a steel beam; if a pilot were to stick his arm out of a window at 400 miles per hour, the wind would snap his arm like a matchstick.

Wind at 500 to 600 miles per hour is equivalent to the blast wave of an atomic explosion close to the blast. It is great enough to smash buildings, including those made of reinforced concrete.

This is why a man is in serious trouble when he tries to bail out of an airplane at such speeds. It is almost impossible to move in the face of the wind. Even if the pilot does manage to get out of his cockpit by crawling into the wind, the airblast is great enough to rock him back—often into the tail of his own airplane—with sufficient force to break his bones, pound him unconscious, and often kill him outright.

Airblast was a grim and lethal enemy in the last years of World War II. Escape became extremely difficult at great speeds. The wind drove fiercely into the cockpit and hammered at the pilot unmercifully. Wind pressure glued him like a fly to his seat or against the side of the airplane.

The pilot had other forces besides wind to fight. If the airplane was undergoing any maneuvers at great speed—even a wide turn—centrifugal force could pin him helplessly to his seat. A force three times that of gravity, easy to achieve in a turn, meant that the pilot could never climb out of his seat.

Worst of all, a crippled airplane often went through wild gyrations. When it did so, the pilot might become helpless. In a spin, when the airplane whirled earthward, he would be pressed against a side of the cockpit. Sometimes the plane

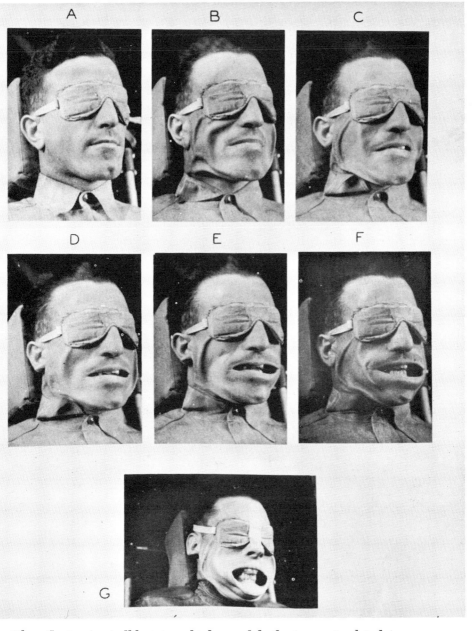

The effects of windblast in a high-speed bailout are simulated in a wind tunnel. Photo A shows the pilot before the wind starts to tear against his face. The force of the wind becomes steadily greater and the effects upon the face are incredible; in Photo C, the pilot can no longer keep his lips closed. Soon his cheeks, ears, and lips flutter wildly. Despite the shocking appearance of the man in Photo G, it's the same pilot in all the pictures. Photo G shows a windblast effect of 310 miles per hour. (U.S. Navy)

tumbled violently; changing forces turned the pilot into a helpless rag doll pounding back and forth within the cockpit with bone-breaking force.

The vital question became: How to get the pilot out with enough control of his senses and his body to deploy his parachute and effect a proper and safe landing?

Air Force and aeronautical engineers tried almost everything in their bag of technical tricks. They made tests in which they deliberately and carefully caused a slow breakup of the airplane in flight. As the airplane fell apart it would rapidly but tolerably decrease its speed in the face of great air pressure. That was true enough, but the airplane, subjected to unequal forces, tumbled and gyrated so violently that it would have killed a man strapped in its cockpit.

Then the engineers examined parachutes. They shot small parachutes back from the tail. Often these snapped free or oscillated wildly. Moreover, by the time they brought the airplane down to a safe bailout speed it could have been entirely enveloped in flames or have been cartwheeling crazily through the air because of structural damage. They tried big parachutes, but they failed to achieve controlled and safe deceleration.

Then they tried a system in which the entire bottom of the airplane fell away, and the pilot in his seat was rammed downward through a sliding chute. They devised systems in which the side of the airplane blew off. But from all their tests and experiments only one system held promise: explosive ejection upward along a guide rail from the cockpit, fast enough and high enough to send the man strapped to his seat well clear of the airplane's tail.

Initial investigations showed that an acceleration twelve times the force of gravity applied to a guide-rail-installed seat would propel seat and pilot upward from the plane with a speed of forty feet per second. This would enable the seat and the pilot safely to clear the airplane.

An experimental method for clearing Navy F3D twin-jet fighter in emergency used a wind-deflector door and a sliding chute. Pilot drops through chute in top photo; clears airplane in center photo; is flung wildly through the air (bottom photo). (U.S. Navy)

212 ⟿| THE SILKEN ANGELS

But would explosive ejection injure, possibly kill, the pilot? How would it affect his spine? Would the seat spin, tumble, or gyrate?

The first scientists to investigate these questions on what we call a hardware basis—for use in operational aircraft—were the Germans. Aware that the jet fighters on which they were working as far back as 1938 would raise speeds to many hundreds of miles per hour, they also anticipated the need for a reliable escape-and-survival system from the forthcoming high-speed machines.

The initial German tests used a compressed air system to fire the seat away from an aircraft. In 1939, the Germans were making manned ejections from modified bombers. Unfortunately for the test subjects, the compressed air guns operated in violent fashion. They struck the pilots agonizing blows, and spinal injuries were commonplace. Almost immediately, the Germans abandoned the compressed air system and went to explosive ejection, using modified 20-mm. cannon shells as the propelling force.

The first ejection seats with the cannon shells went into combat aircraft in 1941. At first their number remained limited, since they were being employed mostly for field testing and experiments under operational and combat conditions, but by 1943 the Germans were saving lives with these early ejection seats. They installed their escape systems in the Heinkel He-219 twin-engine night fighter and the Heinkel He-177 four-engine bomber. The crews of the latter especially had many opportunities to appreciate the ejection seats. The giant Heinkel, with two engines geared together within a single nacelle (so that it looked like a twin-engine airplane), was infamous for its habit of unexpectedly blowing up and burning in the air.

Bad as were the problems with propeller-driven fighters, jets made ordinary bailout techniques almost suicidal. Unless the

Downward ejection seat system in
Stratojet *bomber shows pilot blasting*
away from six-engine bomber flying
at 600 miles per hour at 40,000 feet.
Note seat starting to tumble.
(Air Force)

pilot could slow the airplane to low jet speeds, it proved almost impossible to get out of these aircraft.

One of the few men to survive an emergency bailout from a jet fighter—without an ejection seat—was Tony Levier. Early in 1945, as chief test pilot for Lockheed, Levier was flying a sleek P-80 *Shooting Star* on an engineering test:

It was on this flight that I had my first serious accident, a turbine wheel failure in the engine that cut the tail off the airplane and nearly cost me my life.

I had climbed to 15,000 feet and was on my descent in a high-speed letdown, intending to reach maximum level flight speed for this test at 10,000 feet. It was to be in the neighborhood of 480 miles per hour indicated, which would have put me well up around 575 miles an hour true air speed and at top r.p.m. of the engine, which at that time was around 11,500.

At 11,000 feet the airplane began to shake slightly, and then suddenly without any warning whatsover the nose of the plane dropped downward. Then it swung violently to the left with such force that I was hurled against the side of the cockpit. From there on the plane tumbled crazily through space, violently pitching over and about. It was this behavior, this terrible thing that was happening, that made me realize I had lost the tail of my plane. Then I realized I was going to be killed.

At the rate of speed I had been flying, I knew I must be falling toward the ground very fast. There was no way to judge it, as I could not distinguish between the sky and the ground. My head was becoming flushed from being repeatedly subjected to negative acceleration. At one moment I was thrown against the canopy, and the next moment I would be bashed down into my seat. With this going on, I was unable to gather my wits about me to release the canopy of the plane and try to get out.

The emergency canopy release was within a few inches of my left hand, where I had placed it just the day before in case something like this ever happened. But now I could not even think enough to act, and if I had I doubt I could have commanded myself to do anything about it. Then I realized this was the end,

"At eleven thousand feet, the airplane began to shake slightly, and then suddenly, without any warning whatsoever, the nose of the plane dropped downward. Then it swung violently to the left." Lockheed test pilot Tony Levier describes his sensational escape from an out-of-control P-80 fighter. (Air Force)

and I thought of my wife and children and my family. As these things flashed through my mind, the airplane slowed up and the violent tumbling lessened, and I pulled myself together and went to work on the canopy release.

I grasped it in my right hand and gave it a violent jerk. In my excitement I pulled so hard it slipped from my grasp and dangled loosely on the end of its cable. Now I reached back with my left hand and seized the cable itself and brought it forward over my left shoulder. Taking another firm grip with my right hand I lunged forward with all my might, and this time the canopy came off the airplane.

Now the full force of the slipstream tore at me in the open cockpit as I strove to release myself from my seat. I was buckled in by my safety belt, and it took two slices at the belt buckle to get it free. As the belt released, the plane was upside down and I literally catapulted out of the cockpit. There were no ejection seats in those days, but luck was with me, as I was thrown free of the airplane, still conscious and apparently unharmed.

A quick look at the ground showed me I was still at a safe altitude, so I did not open my parachute right away. I feared I might be falling too fast, and I did not want to take any chances of ripping my chute by opening it at a high speed. Instead I chose to huddle up in a ball and fall free at first to slow up and get away from the plane.

I had fallen like this several seconds when I stretched out to look around, and over to my right I saw the airplane exactly even with me, falling at the same speed I was. It was perhaps a hundred feet away, tumbling through space in crazy fashion, and, sure enough, it didn't have any tail.

It was at this point that I realized it was best to open my parachute, which I did. It opened up fine, although this was only the second jump I had ever made, and I started to think about myself and take stock of my injuries. I had a bad cut on my chin, apparently caused by the buckles on my shoulder straps when I left the airplane, but otherwise I seemed all right. I was about to throw my oxygen mask away, along with the parachute ripcord which I still held in my hand, but it was a perfectly good mask so I tucked it inside my leather flying jacket.

As I neared the ground I started swinging, but I pulled one set of risers and spilled air on one side and it stopped. Then I started swinging close to the ground again, but this time I was too low to check it. I was afraid of dumping the chute. I hoped to hit on the upswing but I didn't. It was just like a high swing on a tree. I swung right into the ground, and it felt like somebody hit me with a sledge hammer. That's when I really damaged myself. There was an excruciating pain in my back, and I fell forward and lay on my stomach for a minute or two until I was sure I was still in one piece. Then I tried to ease the pain by rolling over on my side and then on my back but it didn't help.

After a few minutes, a highway worker came up and asked if he could put the chute under my head to make me more comfortable. "Sure," I said. "I would appreciate it very much." I was in a state of shock, and with no control over myself I began to cry like a baby. . . . In about half an hour I was placed in a jeep and driven over the desert toward Muroc. Part way we were met by an Army ambulance, and they put me in it and drove me to the base hospital some thirty miles away.

As it turned out, Levier's pain came from two crushed vertebrae. He spent five weeks in a hospital bed and then another six months in a steel brace, but he still considers himself lucky.

Early in 1944, the British government discussed ejection seat systems for the new British jets with James Martin. As chief designer of Martin-Baker, James Martin was famous in British engineering circles. "I had heard nothing of the German seats at that time," he explains, "but first had the idea of throwing the pilot clear by a long swinging arm which would be hinged near the rear of the fuselage." Following his American counterparts, Martin quickly abandoned this cumbersome concept and designed an ejection seat system.

For the next two years, the Martin-Baker Company conducted extensive development tests. On July 24, 1947, Bernard Lynch made England's first live ejection from a *Meteor* jet fighter flying at 8000 feet and just over 400 miles per hour. Lynch went back for thirty more live ejections. When the program was over, the British had one of the most reliable ejection systems in existence.

Development in the United States followed the same pattern but was carried out on a much more extensive scale. We ran hundreds of experiments on rails laid down in the desert. How much acceleration and deceleration could a man withstand? To find out, we strapped men on special seats, in many different angles and attitudes, and secured the seats to powerful sleds. The sleds rode on special slippers over the rails, and to push the whole thing along was a second sled, fairly bulging with powerful solid-propellant rockets. The countdowns became endless; the screaming, wild rides down the rails went on one after the other. Men were pushed, squeezed, buffeted, shaken, battered, vibrated, accelerated, slammed to stops; their bones were bent and jerked and twisted and pulled out of place. Over and over and over again they went through these tests, the worst of which was a howling ride by Colonel John Paul Stapp, Jr., to a speed of 632 miles per hour on the ground.

And then Colonel Stapp crashed to a dead stop in exactly 1.4 seconds! The 46.2g load he suffered in his stop was equal to a man blasting free of a jet fighter at 40,000 feet, flying at 1000 miles per hour.

Tests refined the data. If an airplane flew at 500 miles per hour, the seat had to be traveling at sixty feet per second to clear the tail. In tests with 20-mm. and 37-mm. cannon shells providing the boost, back injuries often became the identifying mark of the volunteers, and fractures of vertebrae were not uncommon. Engineers slowed down the push, reducing the tremendous onset of force applied against the spinal column; the trick, they learned, was to transmit the force smoothly instead of in a hard, blasting impact.

There were many different problems. The volunteers and the engineers worked to keep arms and legs from flailing wildly in the savage airblast, for legs and arms were being whipped brutally and snapped or twisted out of their sockets. Some seats had face screens to protect the pilot; the flyer tugged with both hands on a grip handle down in front of his face. This brought a protective windscreen in front of him and simultaneously fired the seat. In this fashion the pilot avoided painful and sometimes injurious twisting of the neck. Other systems used straps and clamps.

There were problems involved in getting pilots out of the seats. Some men never released their grips and plunged all the way to earth in their seats. Some seats had "thumpers": after

In one of the earliest ejection-seat firings of the United States, a test jumper explodes upward from a World War II Invader bomber over the California desert. Note the seat and pilot just above the airplane. (U.S. Navy)

a certain time interval, the pilot's hands or knuckles were rapped sharply by metal bars, reminding him to let go. He had only to reach down and release a catch for his belt and shoulder straps, and he would fall away from the seat.

Some seats had automatic ejection systems of their own. As the pilot fell, a series of automatic devices were alerted to protect him. If he bailed out at high altitude, a barometric release was triggered as he fell (usually at 14,000 feet). A tension spring suddenly wound up, and a strap on which the pilot was sitting snapped taut, flinging him out of the seat.

But as important as anything else was the timer that opened the parachute automatically. If a man bailed out at 38,000 feet, he knew that to open his parachute at this height could be fatal—that for his own survival he had to fall freely through the air. But what if he blacked out during the fall; what if he were wounded or his emergency oxygen system failed to work?

The key to survival lay in a barometric pressure device. It was set at 14,000 feet, at which height it automatically pulled the ripcord and opened the parachute, even if the pilot were unconscious.

The new systems were ingenious, and they compensated for both high- and low-altitude bailout.

Before takeoff, a pilot set the timer release mechanism of his parachute. When flying at low altitude, it was set for "immediate" or one-second action. Immediately after separating from his seat, the ripcord pulled to open the parachute. This assured no wasted time in deploying the chute. If he flew at medium or high altitude, he set the chute at a two-second interval, leaving him plenty of time to clear the seat. If he bailed out above 14,000 feet, the barometric safety release kept the chute from opening until he fell to 14,000 feet. Below that altitude, the release was bypassed and the chute operated on the time-interval system.

The first man in the United States to eject from a jet fighter was Major Vincent Mazza of the Air Force. He rode in the

In this remarkably clear photo of a test firing of new ejection seat from Navy TV-2, the pilot has just exploded away from the airplane; note the pilot holding windscreen before his face. Pulling down on the screen actuates the ejection system.
(U.S. Navy)

---

rear seat of a T-33 jet trainer. Flying at 555 miles per hour, two miles over San Francisco Bay, he blasted out of the jet—and landed safely in the water just ten minutes later.

But Mazza ejected under carefully established conditions. An actual emergency in a jet fighter would not permit time-consuming preparations.

CHAPTER 15

Eject!

To THE PILOT of a heavy, sweptwing, and supersonic jet fighter, escape from his aircraft in emergency situations can never be the same: the conditions under which he will be forced to explosively eject himself from his machine always vary.

The "classic" of all escape problems may be said to take place in the heavy jet fighter when its speed is dangerously low, its power is almost gone, and the ground is ready to scrape at the belly of the airplane. Add to this the problems of control or equipment failure, explosions, or fire, and it is not difficult to understand why low-altitude ejections account for the greatest number of fatalities among our fighter pilots.

Safety officers warn new pilots (and old pilots as well) that from ground level to a height of 5000 feet above the terrain the odds against surviving emergencies are longest. If nothing else, the very speed at which the jet fighter moves means that precious altitude disappears within seconds. The time required to carry out emergency procedures also eats into the little time available to the pilot in which to save his life. The ejection process, clearing the airplane, clearing the seat, deploying the parachute canopy—all these add up to insufficient time before impact with the ground.

Experienced pilots know that the key to survival at low altitude is instant decision followed by instant action.

"The pilot encounters his most dangerous moments of flight as he takes off from the ground," explained a flight safety officer to me at Nellis Air Force Base. "At this moment his engine gives him everything it has in the way of power, but it still adds up only to minimum flight speed. So he faces a combination of factors which add up to danger. At the very moment that he becomes airborne, he is still at zero altitude with zero speed. He lacks the altitude which he can exchange for speed, and he hasn't any speed to trade for altitude. You might say the situation is rather uncompromising.

"Fortunately for the pilot, the jets—especially today—really leap off; they get up and go with tremendous acceleration. This means that the pilot can narrow down that uncompromising situation to the very minimum number of seconds. But, being frank about it, if things go wrong here the pilot is on a very narrow tightrope of survival. He's got to evaluate his situation, make a decision based upon his evaluations, and then take whatever action is necessary to carry out his decision. He's got less time to do this than I've spent in describing it to you."

One pilot added a postscript: "Being what we are, men make mistakes. Down here in this tight survival corridor, that kind of mistake can—and *does*—kill."

In my close association with Air Force fighter pilots, I know several men who have ejected from jet fighter planes, sometimes under the most perilous of conditions. Because of our close friendship, it has been possible to obtain many of the details of such an event that normally never find their way into the official records.

One such pilot is an especially old and close friend, Captain Joseph W. Kittinger, USAF. Joe Kittinger had the unique opportunity—as a test pilot with extensive parachute jumping experience—to compare the differences between jumping under

The ejection seat and escape system of the hypersonic X-15 is tested. An exact replica of the X-15 nose section hurtles down a track at hundreds of miles per hour; dummy pilot is fired in the seat. Canopy has just blown away (top right), and powerful rocket tube is blasting seat upwards from the cockpit. (Air Force)

desired conditions and a situation in which an emergency "added frantic haste to my actions."

Joe took off from a desert runway in an F-100C *Super Sabre* jet fighter, a huge brute that weighs more than 28,000 pounds and that is described by its pilots as a "very big and very heavy piece of machinery." The tower cleared Joe to start his roll; he moved the throttle forward to Full Military Power, released the brakes, and started down the runway. As the airplane moved, Joe shoved the throttle into afterburner position, and 16,000 pounds thrust kicked the *Super Sabre* on its way.

These big fighters (I have flown in the two-seat F-100F version of Joe's fighter) get going with a deceptive acceleration. To the pilot wearing the heavy helmet, and with the engine sound behind the cockpit, it seems that very little is happening. The push is quiet, but events take place with the speed of a great boulder accelerating down a steep mountainside. It is hard to believe the moment of takeoff in one of these slab-winged monsters. The pilot doesn't pull back on the control stick; he gives it just the barest nudge toward him, and then— well, the airplane seems to stay still, but the earth falls down into a hole below the wings!

As the F-100C lifted its nose and began to grab for altitude, Joe hit the gear retraction lever. Normally the wheels snap inward and upward, thumping into recessed wells, and are then covered with flush doors and panels. With the gear out of the way, drag is reduced, and acceleration becomes extremely rapid.

But on this flight the gear stayed down. At once the fighter lost its hydraulic pressure. Joe watched the gauge swing around from 3000 pounds per square inch to a useless zero. But at least he had power, and very quickly Joe kept the nose sucked up and went for precious height. When the needle read 5500 feet he knew he was 1500 feet over the desert floor, and that gave him a slight margin of safety.

There is a saying that, with just a little ungluing, a small

This photo sequence of jet combat—and the kill of a Russian MiG-15 fighter—is extremely rare. At top left, MiG has been crippled. In top center, column of fire is explosive charge of ejection seat firing. At top right, pilot and seat have just cleared the airplane. Bottom sequence shows continuing separation of the pilot from his airplane. The airplane was flying at better than 600 miles per hour when these pictures were taken by gun camera. (Air Force)

emergency can become a thundering catastrophe in no time at all. And this is what happened now to Joe. No sooner did he level off when a red light flashed the warning of an over-heating engine. For the next minute or so he fought the air-plane, trying to joggle the throttle in and out of its overheating condition, trying to check if the gear was locked in the down position, trying to stay in a turn by the runways, and trying also to keep from stalling—any one of these enough to keep a man entirely occupied. All together they create a situation where a man needs about six hands, each one busily attending to vital matters.

Joe quit worrying about all of this when the control stick went crazy in his hands. The stick started to move back, bringing up the nose and lowering the forward airspeed. Joe pushed against the stick, but it was no use. The fighter was getting away from him; systems were failing throughout the airplane; and very quickly it would be the runaway F-100C that was boss, not Joe.

The stick had moved back slowly; now it slammed back to-ward Joe, and the fighter reared, nose upward. Almost at once it shuddered and groaned through its length—stall!

"At this altitude the stall was suicide," Joe explained to me. "My hands seemed to flash among the emergency controls with a mind of their own. The shudder came again, and I knew clearly that I was just about out of any time I had left. I was only eight hundred feet over the ground, losing altitude fast, and I could hear a voice shouting at me in my brain to 'Get out! Get out *now!*' I didn't wait any more. I *got.*"

The *Super Sabre* wallowed helplessly in the air, hanging grimly to the last shreds of lift with her wings, getting ready to make its final dip and fiery contact with the ground.

I grasped the seat handle and squeezed the canopy release. A tremendous roar exploded into the cockpit. In that instant, the wind snatched the helmet from my head and whisked it away. I noticed this almost as though I were watching from a distance.

A powerful and heavy Super Sabre *fighter of this type "ran away" from test pilot Captain Joe Kittinger. The engine burned and the controls froze; at 800 feet he exploded himself away from the stricken airplane in safe ejection.* (North American Aviation)

The wind was a continuing, explosive roar. I couldn't find the seat-ejection trigger in the right arm grip. Time—no time left. But I looked for it. I jerked my head back against the rest. Feet in the stirrups, chin down, arms on the rests. I squeezed the trigger.

The seat flashed up and away from the airplane. Strange: I felt no kick, no force of the powerful explosion that blasted me out of the airplane. The next thing I knew I was tumbling through the air. The commands flashed through my mind, as if another voice were shouting to me. The belt on my lap; I reached down to release the belt, to get away from the seat.

No belt: the seat was already gone! I don't remember what I saw at this moment. I moved by reflex, grabbing for the ripcord. I never pulled the ring; even before I could think about it the parachute cracked open! There wasn't even a jolt, not a sensation, as the canopy boomed out, full and taut. I remember I was scared; physically, I didn't feel a thing.

The moment the canopy opened, however, I distinctly heard the roar of the jet engine. This was the first impression I received. I turned in the harness and watched as the fighter wallowed helplessly. She fishtailed with her nose high, yawing from side to side. Still in this position, she dropped like a rock and plunged into the ground. A searing ball of flame mushroomed upward and boomed into the sky; at this same instant my feet hit the ground, a quarter mile away from the fireball. I rolled over and rose to my feet. I didn't have a scratch on me.

The next morning the other pilots saw Joe walking down the flight line toward the parachute rigging and packing shed, with the biggest and finest bottle of Scotch he could buy, for the man who had packed his chute.

Captain Chuck Maultsby is an Air Force jet fighter pilot who became known to millions of Americans as the Right Wing of the Air Force Thunderbirds aerobatic team. When I lived and flew with the Thunderbirds in 1960, Maultsby's skill not only gained the plaudits of the throngs who watched the team in their fabulous demonstrations of jet precision flying, but also the deep respect of his fellow pilots. And there just isn't any higher to go in gaining the respect of other pilots than *that*.

But long before he joined the Thunderbirds, Chuck Maultsby had known another kind of flying that added some special thrills of its own: the fighter-bomber missions in Korea that called for slugging it out at treetop level with Chinese flak that could turn the sky into a great bowl of crackling flak bursts.

Maultsby took off one morning from the K-13 advanced airfield at Sumon, Korea, with two 1000-pound bombs beneath the wings of his F-80 *Shooting Star*. The jet airplane he flew didn't respond nicely to the load of fuel, guns, and bombs; it groaned its way into the sky, gaining some decent responsiveness to the controls only after speed built up and the ground fell steadily away. Or at least it should have, but not today. Chuck cursed quietly in the cockpit. An electrical short in the control system jammed the elevator trim into a nose-up position. The fighter wanted to pitch up its nose and climb steeply, which would have meant a stall and a crash. Chuck Maultsby could have—should have—jettisoned his bombs and called it a day. He didn't do this; instead, he pushed hard forward on the stick and held formation. He knew he would have to hold hard stick forward all the way to the target and all the way back, and when he got down on the ground his arm would be absolutely numb with pain. This was his seventeenth mission.

Kunri was a trap. The Chinese armed Kunri with dozens of light and heavy guns, including several batteries of deadly, accurate 88-mm. flak guns. Kunri was a bristling wall of explosive flak just waiting to go off.

The fighter bombers circled the target, and the pilots stared at the heavy anti-aircraft barrage erupting from the ground. Great clouds of oily black smoke, their centers splotched angrily with red, blossomed everywhere in the sky. Tracers hosed in broken flashes toward the airplanes. The squadron leader ordered a dive-bombing attack.

Chuck Maultsby rolled over almost on his back and shoved

the F-80 into a steep dive. At an angle of 60 degrees a heavy shell crashed into the side of the airplane, and the world seemed to blow up in his face. At the moment of the explosion, Chuck was concentrating all his attention on the rail lines with their freight cars packed with supplies. Then the fantastic shock smashed through the airplane, slamming Chuck with a giant hand against the side of the canopy.

The shell exploded just about seven feet behind the pilot. The blast ripped forward into the throttle quadrant, dissolved the instrument panel, and transformed the windscreen into a blur of cracked glass. Sharp thuds slammed into the back of the seat; the armor plating saved Maultsby's life, stopping a barrage of jagged shards of metal.

At the same instant a flash fire whipped through the cockpit, and Chuck stared down at his left arm, wrapped completely in flames. He stuck his left arm straight out into the air; the windblast snuffed out the fire.

And that was when he realized through the numbing shock of the explosion what he had done. He had extended his arm to the side *into the air*.

Fate had intervened in his behalf. The original plan called for a glide-bombing run in a shallow descent. In the glide-bombing attack, Chuck would have flown with his hand on the throttle, on the left side of the cockpit.

"The decision to dive bomb is the only reason I have a left arm today," he recalled. "When the shell hit the bird, it blew out the whole side of the airplane, throttle quadrant and all. Because of the dive mission, my hand was at that moment on the gunsight, right up forward, just above the instrument panel. I was changing the depression of the sight. In glide bombing you need more depression on the sight to predict the bomb fall; dive bombing, however, is virtually line-of-sight."

Several things happened almost simultaneously. Chuck snuffed out the fire on his arm and almost at the same moment

Overloaded with full fuel tanks, tip tanks, two 1000-lb. bombs, and full ammunition loads, Shooting Stars *head for Communist targets in North Korea. Chuck Maultsby had a miraculous escape from a shattered, burning fighter like these—and landed safely.* (Air Force)

realized that he had no control. The stick was useless, flopping about in the cockpit.

Chuck Maultsby was diving straight into the earth, out of control, without enough time to get out of the plunging fighter.

But the circuit breaker that he had cursed so soundly before now became another factor in saving his life. The instant the shell burst knocked out the elevator control, it eliminated the effect of Chuck's forward pressure on the stick. The airplane was trimmed out to a nose-up attitude, and the instant the controls were severed, the airplane responded to the trim and pitched *up.* Chuck had just enough time to squeeze the bomb release and send his two 1000-pounders into the target. Then, the effect of the lightened load and the full trim turned the pitchup into a violent maneuver.

It was so violent that the G forces rammed Chuck's head down between his knees. His legs were straight out. He couldn't lift his head, he had no throttle with which to chop the speed of the fighter. His hands grasped the ejection handles and yanked back, hard. As he pulled to actuate the explosive charge, he remembered with a flash of horror that this is the way a pilot loses both legs, sliced crudely off at the knees, by their being smashed against the front edge of the upper canopy. It was not a pleasant thought, but he had no choice.

And then—another stroke of luck—as the seat exploded out of the airplane, it tumbled, and it tumbled forward. It was seemingly impossible, but the tumble caused Chuck's legs to miss the sharp canopy edge, perhaps by no more than the barest fraction of an inch.

The airstream struck with a terrific roar at his ears. The sky and horizon tumbled crazily before his eyes. He had no automatic devices on his seat. He was at low altitude. He released the belt, threshed his legs wildly, and kicked the seat away from his tumbling body. The pilot chute snapped away automatically, dragged out the canopy in a long streamer, and then a great *crack!* In that instant the tumbling flight ended, and Chuck was suspended beneath the ballooning silk.

It should have been quiet; other pilots have described the sensation of drifting earthward in this manner and the quiet sighing of the wind. Instead, there was a terrifying din: a "tremendous, constant crackling roar in the sky." Three squadrons of jet fighters screamed earthward, engines howling. A forest of anti-aircraft guns blasted away in an unceasing cannonade of sound. Bombs smashed into the earth, the concussion waves rippling out and slapping at Chuck's body and causing the chute to twitch and jerk.

The earth was covered with snow. Chuck drifted down beneath a chute that was all white; if it had been red the other

Captain Charles "Chuck" Maultsby, USAF, was one of the out-standing pilots in the famed Air Force Thunderbirds jet aerobatic team. Maultsby, surviving hairline escape from blazing fighter in Korea and "unpleasant" treatment for many months in Chinese prison camps, returned to join Thunderbirds. Today this outstand-ing pilot flies advanced jet aircraft missions for the Air Force. (Air Force)

236 ✈ THE SILKEN ANGELS

pilots could have seen him and known that he had ejected safely. But he was invisible to them.

He floated to earth directly into the center of the target. At the same moment, a half-dozen 1000-pound bombs struck the ground, and Chuck was in the center of a hell of explosions and waves of concussion.

"I hate to say it, but it's a good thing those guys couldn't hit what they were aiming at," he mused in recollection, "because they sure as hell would have killed me. On the way down, I thought the Chinese were shooting at me. The chute was riddled with holes, and I could even hear the bullets passing right by my ears. But they weren't; they were just firing madly with every gun they had at the planes."

His body fell into the snow, and he quickly slipped from the parachute harness and dashed madly away from the target center. He did not run very far. Two bombs exploding less than a hundred yards away churned the earth into a thundering volcano. A great fist smashed him to the ground.

Dazed, he climbed to his feet and started to run again, trying to reach a knoll from where he could make an escape. But there were twelve airplanes in their dives, and the bombs continued to smash into the earth. Every time he got to his feet and ran, the shock waves hammered him down to the ground.

When he finally reached the knoll, too much time had passed. He looked up into the muzzles of a dozen rifles, all held by Chinese soldiers and all pointed at him. It was the beginning of twenty-two months as a prisoner of war of the Chinese.

Not all ejections and escapes are successful. Sometimes even the most skilled of pilots is deserted by Lady Luck, and then all the skill and courage in the world are no good at all. A part of our story concerns the death of a superb flier. This was Captain Charles Salmon of the Thunderbirds, whom everyone called Fish. He was the kind of a pilot that other men who flew called "one of the greats." He joined the Thunderbirds early in 1958, as the Solo Pilot of the team, and then moved into the slot (trailing) position of the diamond formation.

"People instinctively liked the guy," one of the Thunderbird pilots said. "He looked like a Hollywood version of a fighter pilot—handsome, winning smile, that sort of thing. He was six foot one and weighed about 210 pounds, a big, happy guy who had a tremendous sense of humor. As a solo pilot he had flair, timing, and the execution of his maneuvers were cut with a razor, they were so precise."

On March 12, 1959, the Thunderbirds were out over the desert on a training mission. Sometimes even the best make just a slight mistake, and this was one of those times. Coming out of a turn, racked over steeply in vertical banks, one *Super Sabre* inched slightly out of line. The pilots saw what was happening and tried to skid and maneuver out of the way. They avoided a major collision; Fish Salmon's fighter struck a glancing blow against that of Chuck Maultsby. The impact tore away the long Pitot boom in front of Maultsby's airplane, sending it through the air inlet right into the engine. The engine growled and choked, but Maultsby nursed it back to Nellis Air Force Base for a safe landing.

The impact also sheared off the top eighteen inches of the vertical stabilizer and rudder from Salmon's airplane. Reacting immediately, he put the fighter into a howling climb, grabbing for altitude. The glancing impact had taken place just above ground level, and that meant trouble, so Fish poured the coal to the fighter and climbed for the safety of height. He went all the way to 30,000 feet and then eased in a turn toward the home field. Damaged plane or not, he was going to try and save the fighter.

The other pilots examined his airplane; they flew in tight and visually checked over the F-100C. The big machine vibrated badly, but it flew, and it responded to the controls. Wisely, Salmon decided to check the fighter's reactions to a condition in which he would lower the landing gear and simulate an approach and landing. At 30,000 feet this would give him a safety margin for escape in case something went wrong. And it did. As the gear came down at 260 miles per hour, the altered airflow and the damaged tail proved too much; the combination snapped the *Super Sabre* into a wicked spin.

Fish brought up the gear and recovered from the spin. His altitude now was 23,000 feet. But no sooner was he out of the spin when the nose swooped up, and the fighter clawed over on a wing to plunge into another spin. Again Fish brought her out, and again she went back into the spin. As he spun and recovered, spun and recovered, the other Thunderbirds circled him. Finally, at 14,000 feet, Major Robert Fitzgerald, Thunderbird leader, warned, "Get ready to get out of that thing, Fish."

She whipped through four more turns.

Fitzgerald called anxiously, "Fish, let it go! Get out of there! Bail out, *now!*"

Fish blew off the canopy, and immediately afterward seat and pilot came shooting out of the spinning airplane. Fish separated almost at once from the seat, and almost in the same motion his parachute streamed out.

And right there was the killer. Flying at low altitude, Fish had had his parachute timer set on zero lanyard: immediate opening of the chute. When he climbed to high altitude, in the excitement of trying to save the damaged airplane he had forgotten to move the zero lanyard to the delayed opening. That proved to be his undoing.

"We're not sure of what happened, not exactly," Chuck Maultsby told me. "But because of the chute opening instantly, and the effects of the spin—well, whatever it was, for some unknown reason the heavy seat drifted up and tore right through the canopy. The chute never opened fully.

The body of Fish Salmon crashed into the boulder-strewn country near Nellis Air Force Base.

In razor-sharp formation, four Super Sabres *of the Thunderbirds streak over Nevada desert in training flight. Captain Charles "Fish" Salmon was flying a* Super Sabre *when a collision broke up the formation. Salmon climbed to high altitude, made successful ejection, but was doomed when ejection seat ripped upward and tore through his parachute canopy.* (Air Force)

If an "impossible" moment of fate had condemned Charles Salmon to die, an equally impossible moment of fate spared the life of another pilot, George F. Smith, a test pilot for North American Aviation.

Smith was flying an older model F-100A off the California coast when his airplane began to ease over into a dive. Just as Joe Kittinger encountered mysterious control failure in the stick moving back and pulling the airplane up into a climb, so Smith found his stick moving forward and, despite frantic attempts to pull the nose up, he found the fighter going into an uncontrollable, screaming dive.

Smith literally could see only seconds in which to save his life. The big fighter went faster and faster until it edged into supersonic speed. Moving frenziedly in the cockpit, Smith managed to blast himself free with a margin of survival of less than two seconds; any delay of two seconds would have meant certain death.

At a speed of 777 miles per hour—1140 feet per second—Smith blew himself out of the plunging airplane. At the moment he ejected he was only 6500 feet above the ocean, or less than five seconds away from a crash. The airplane was still accelerating, and the time left before the impact was being cut down rapidly.

George Smith became the first human being to survive ejection from a jet fighter flying at supersonic speed. Doctors say that not one but a combination of miracles kept George Smith alive.

At his speed and altitude, airblast was no longer simply a force. It had become, instead, a solid and massive wall in the sky, and into this wall George Smith crashed with terrifying impact. The terrible blow he suffered as his body shot into the airstream smashed him unconscious almost instantly.

A series of strange events snatched Smith from death. Of all the parachutes—and there were hundreds—kept at the test base for pilots, only two were fully automatic. Smith had one of those chutes. An automatic separation device flung his unconscious body away from the seat, and immediately afterward another automatic device pulled the ripcord.

No one knows how that parachute ever remained in enough pieces to bring Smith down alive. As it was, the terrible jolt of the opening chute ripped panels away, cut and slashed at the nylon. The parachute stopped with a force forty times that of gravity! The vicious 40g jolt increased Smith's body weight to 8800 pounds. So violent were the forces involved that his tight-fitting gloves, wrist watch, and a ring were ripped from his body.

His unconscious form reached the ocean in brutal condition. His clothes were slashed to ribbons. His gloves, watch, ring, shoes, and socks had vanished, as well as his strong helmet and his oxygen mask. His feet were slashed and bleeding. A severe cut on his forehead bled copiously. His lips were blue from bruises, and leaking blood.

He was, in fact, more dead than alive, and in severe shock. He bled so severely in his eyeballs that he was blind for days, and all that could be seen of his eyes was a solid red mass. Almost his entire body was covered with welts, bruises, and cuts. The airblast had violently attacked his lips, ears, and eyelids; they were pounded and then slashed open. His entire face was distorted grotesquely and colored a dark purple from serious bleeding beneath the skin. His flailing legs had pulled his knee joints completely loose.

Internal damage was severe. Doctors had to operate almost at once on his lower intestine. His liver had sustained brutal damage. And this is only part of the agony he suffered. For weeks he was in serious condition and in constant pain.

Yet he lived. And he went back to flying.

Other men have ejected under "impossible" conditions and lived. New types of ejection systems—longer-burning rockets instead of explosive shells, for example—greatly increase a pilot's chances for survival under the worst of circumstances.

In April, 1957, Flying Officer M. Thurley of the Royal Air Force was landing a Hunter jet fighter for an emergency wheels-up touchdown. No sooner did the airplane strike the ground than it began to fall apart on the runway. The force of the breakup proved so great that the shock triggered the ejection seat. The unusual ignition (as it may be called) actually saved Thurley's life. The disintegrating airplane ended up as a fiery mass of wreckage tearing down the runway, but Thurley was out, soaring up and around with an opening parachute. He came out of his wild adventure with only minor injuries, and you can't bail out any lower than he did!

French test pilot André Morel just about did Thurley's miraculous escape one better. He was flying the experimental *Coleoptre*, a vertical takeoff and landing aircraft. Just above the ground, at zero forward speed, the engine failed. Morel lacked both height and speed, but the instant the machine dropped clumsily he fired himself out of the helpless craft. The parachute boomed open, and the very next second Morel's feet were on the runway.

But there are few pilots who will ever want to repeat the experience of Flying Officer Peter Underdown. In 1954, flying a *Sabre* jet fighter over Holland, Underdown's airplane began to go to pieces. It literally disintegrated in mid-air at a speed of more than 400 miles per hour. Strapped tightly into his seat, Underdown was flung violently into the airstream. He was so low that before he could ever make a move with his hands he crashed, still in the seat, into an orchard.

The orchard stood on a long, steeply sloping hill. Underdown smashed into the first tree traveling backwards and tilted slightly head back, the only position that could have helped him. In a fantastic scene, the seat sped through the orchard, its angle of fall matching exactly the angle of slope of the orchard!

George Smith's plummeting Super Sabre *looked like this when the North American test pilot ejected at 777 miles per hour only 6500 feet above the earth. Extraordinary picture shows the supersonic shock wave behind diving airplane. Smith ejected into a windblast of 1140 feet per second, suffered a terrible jolt of forty times gravity —and survived!* (North American Aviation)

He thundered through the trees no more than a dozen feet off the ground, slicing through one tree after the other like some huge and deadly battering ram, sending leaves and branches flying in all directions. Abruptly the seat pounded to a stop in the fork of one apple tree, solidly wedged in the fork, with Underdown still inside, bruised and shaken but otherwise in perfect shape! He was entirely conscious and was calling for help to the farmer who ran to the scene, expecting to find a dead, battered form.

For several minutes the farmer stared incredulously, mouth agape, at the gesticulating, shouting pilot.

There is also the case of the pilot who ejected from his airplane *below* the surface of the ocean. On October 13, 1954, Lieutenant B. Macfarlane of the Royal Navy performed this incredible feat. He flew from the British aircraft carrier HMS *Albion;* one morning he was catapulted from the carrier in a Wyvern aircraft.

The slingshot effect of the catapult hurled him off the bow of the carrier, and at the same moment the Wyvern's engine failed completely, losing all power. It plunged into the sea like an enormous boulder, smashing into the water in a nose-down attitude.

Almost immediately, as the airplane sank, the carrier crashed overhead—and cut the airplane in two pieces. Despite this tremendous shock and the violence of the carrier's thrashing propellers, at a depth of twenty feet Macfarlane in desperation fired his ejection seat. The canopy spun out of the way, the seat surged out and upward from the cockpit. It didn't move far, but it was far enough for Macfarlane to release his straps and pop to the surface. Injuries? They were minor!

Several men have already ejected from their aircraft at extreme heights, but not all of these pilots have survived the abrupt contrast of the confines of a pressurized cockpit with the low atmospheric pressure of 40,000 feet and above. Jet fighters today protect the pilot with complete pressurization systems, so that while the airplane is flying at 40,000 feet, the pressure inside the airplane may be only that of 20,000 or 25,000 feet. One pilot ejected at 40,000—and he was not wearing a pressure suit about his body. He survived the ejection and his descent to earth, but the explosive expansion of gases within his body proved to be fatal. His internal organs were ruptured severely, and he died less than twenty-four hours later in the hospital.

On October 10, 1959, British test pilot Johnny Squire thundered at 40,000 feet over the Irish Channel in an English *Electric Lightning* fighter. The huge airplane streaked along at 1500 miles per hour, booming through the sky at more than twice the speed of sound. Suddenly the big *Lightning* "ran away" from its pilot.

At this speed any abrupt or awkward control maneuvers can tear the airplane to pieces or cause it to explode violently. Squire didn't waste a second. As the supersonic jet began to vibrate and yaw dangerously, he blew himself out of the airplane, the first ejection ever made at such a stupendous speed. His pressure suit saved him from severe physical injury. Squire rode his seat for a while, then pushed clear and opened his parachute. He splashed down in the Channel.

If this weren't bad enough, worse was the fact that no one could find him. The tough pilot not only survived a Mach 2 plus bailout at 40,000 feet, but he struggled for two days and nights in his little one-man dinghy until he finally paddled ashore!

Squire's ejection was not the highest in England. Two other pilots were forced to abandon their airplane at 56,000 feet! The two men, P. F. de Salis and P. H. G. Lowe, were flying a Canberra bomber that was boosted well into the stratosphere by two blazing rocket engines. Fifty-six thousand feet up, de Salis lost control of the airplane. It slewed violently in the thin air and began to break up into pieces. Both men ejected—and again, their pressure suits kept them alive and protected them against the bitter cold and the effects of explosive decompression. Both men landed safely.

No one man understands better the life-or-death difference of the pressure suit in a high-altitude bailout than Marine Colonel William H. Rankin. He was flying at nearly 50,000 feet in an F8U *Crusader* jet fighter when he suddenly lost all power and all control function.

Colonel Rankin had no choice but to eject, and it was into a sea of agony that he burst. He wore only a summer flying suit, gloves, and a pilot's helmet. More than one pilot has questioned why the Marine pilot ever flew to this height without a pressure suit, and Colonel Rankin had good reason to regret its absence. In the cockpit the temperature was a comfortable 75 degrees Fahrenheit. Outside the cockpit it was 70 degrees below zero, a temperature difference of 145 degrees! And it was into this bitterly cold air that the Marine blasted himself when he lost all control of his fighter.

His first impression, he told doctors later, was that his body instantly became a "freezing, expanding mass of pain." He said that the cold struck his body like a million tiny knives. Bad as was the cold, the wind smashed into his body with a speed of several hundred miles per hour, creating an effect of cold that the colonel called "unbelievable."

Even worse was the effect of the explosive decompression, which he said was "unbearable." The expansion of gases and body fluids within his abdomen stretched it out so suddenly and violently that he looked like a huge swollen ball and was deathly afraid that his abdomen "would burst."

He felt as if his eyes would rip clear from their sockets. Violent pains assailed his head; it felt as if his skull were cracking into pieces. Knifelike cramps ripped through his body, and terrible pain filled his ears.

As he fell, embraced in a pain that felt as though he had been plunged into live flames, his stomach stretched out more.

His clothes were grotesquely pushed out of shape from the enormous expansion of his stomach, an expansion he described as "savage pain." The decompression slashed and ripped open blood vessels, and he bled from his eyes, ears, nose, and mouth.

Wracked with agony, bleeding, severely injured internally, he finally reached the earth—safe, but not sound.

Doctors said that it was a miracle that he was alive. The colonel recovered, survivor of one of the most fantastic personal experiences ever encountered with the silken angel.

Flying a Crusader *jet fighter, Marine Colonel William H. Rankin, without any protective clothing or equipment, ejected at an altitude of 50,000 feet into a temperature of minus 70 degrees. He said later that his body instantly became a "freezing, expanding mass of pain."* (U.S. Navy)

CHAPTER 16

From a Killer Spin to the Greatest Jump

CAPTAIN JOSEPH W. KITTINGER, USAF, is a man whom we met briefly in the preceding chapter, as the survivor of an emergency ejection only 800 feet above the desert, when he blew himself out of a crippled jet fighter. But Joe Kittinger is an almost immortal figure in the world of men and parachutes, for he is the man who has made the longest free-fall jumps of any man in the world. As part of an Air Force research effort known as Project Excelsior, Joe made a series of jumps from balloons that drifted to the edge of space. His test leaps were to find a way for an untrained pilot to abandon an airplane from 60,000 to 100,000 feet above the earth and fall freely to low altitude and dense air before deploying his main parachute.

Earlier in our story, in Chapter 10, we discussed the killer spin, the violent flat rotation of the human body as it falls through the air, the spin that snares men in its centrifugal trap, and spins them all the way to their death.

In August of 1944, Lieutenant Colonel Melbourne W. Boynton of the Army Air Forces jumped from 42,000 feet. It was a free-fall jump; Boynton was determined to prove that a man could retain full control of his body and his mind on the way down. The Russians already had jumped from 40,000 feet; Boynton had no worry about his safety.

He was wrong. His body whirled into a spin. Faster and faster he went, until the blood pooled in his head and his brain became useless . . . and a long time later, his body whirled into the ground like a propeller blade.

In 1950, Major Vincent Mazza, who had made the first ejection in the United States from a jet fighter, took up where Boynton had left off. He jumped from 41,586 feet and, in full control of his body, dropped to low altitude before opening his parachute. Mazza and his research group felt that if a man could control his body by doubling into a V-shape at the waist, the spinning and tumbling would be reduced to the minimum.

Subsequently, other researchers proved that this information, even were it valid, has little to do with emergency ejections from extremely high altitude. An injured pilot, a man in a daze, cannot be expected to maintain precise control over his body. And even if he could, it takes tremendous experience to learn all the little tricks of high jumps in order to survive.

Joe Kittinger got the job of testing a new stabilization device called the Beaupre parachute. To the regular parachute, Francis Beaupre added his own design, a small six-foot stabilization canopy. The canopy would open just prior to the falling body reaching terminal velocity. At terminal velocity the spins usually began. If this could be kept from happening, even though the man still fell freely, then he could be completely stabilized all the way down, even if he were unconscious or otherwise helpless. The automatic barometric system of the parachute would open the main canopy at 14,000 feet—and the silken angel would live up to its name.

Kittinger planned on three jumps with Project Excelsior. On his first ascent in an open gondola, suspended beneath a great balloon, he rose to 76,000 feet. In his own words, here is the personal story of one of the most incredible parachute sagas in the history of flight:

I stand in the gondola. . . . Now that the radios are disconnected, I am cut off from the world 76,000 feet below. The lack of sound is almost a crash of silence. Something penetrates the emptiness, a wheezing that hisses directly in my ears. It is the sound of my own breathing in the pressure helmet.

I shuffle clumsily to the narrow opening and stop. I am incredibly awkward (weighing over 250 pounds with equipment). Now I bend my trunk forward just slightly to place my arms outside the thin aluminum wall of the gondola, in space.

I grasp the lanyard which is attached to the two timers of my parachute. This is my final connection to the gondola, the last of the umbilical cords to be severed. With my right hand—clumsily, because of the restricting confines of the pressure suit—I make a hard, outward, pulling motion. I stare at the lanyard in disbelief: the arming timers fail to pull free!

Quickly I pull again, as hard as I can. A third time—and finally the timer knobs pull free. With a short, disgusted motion I fling them away from me. I reach back for my final task aboard the gondola and punch the button that starts all the data cameras running.

I hesitate for a moment and grant myself that time to look down at the earth, 76,000 feet below me . . . and take a small, ludicrous short hop.

I fall away from the balloon, face down and arms out, staring at the earth. I am unaware that I hold my breath.

There is no sound. Not a whisper of wind. No vibration. Nothing. *Nothing?*

No sensation . . . absolutely no sensation at all. I cannot be falling! This cannot be real. . . . My thoughts whirl crazily. Something fantastic, impossible, is happening to me. A roaring that is without sound thunders in my brain.

I do not move. . . . *I'm not falling!*

Never have I known or even remotely dreamed of anything like this. I stare, hard. I think my eyes are bulging in their sockets. The world is insane.

There is only . . . nothing. The flatness is far below, frozen in time and space. My brain spins; time itself has ground to a halt.

That earth down there, so far below—I want desperately, with all my heart and soul, to *fall*.

What is happening to me?

It is as though God looked down and for some reason inexplicable to me, far beyond any comprehension I might ever receive, He reached out and stopped the world and time and space and everything in it from moving.

There is no time. Never before, never again, will I know the freezing numbness of unreality that steals through my mind and body. Seconds . . . hours . . . no time.

Then comes the first intrusion into the void. A vibration, a tiny tremor that starts at my back. I hear the sound, feel the vibration through my body. What is——

The timer for the stabilization chute! But . . . how long has it been since I stepped out of the gondola? It cannot be time yet.

I take a grip on my chaotic thoughts. The reality of the moment is the vibration of the timer. Instinctively, I tense for the parachute to pull free, for the canopy to deploy to its diameter of six feet; I wait for the slight tug.

Nothing happens.

I wait . . . again an *absence* of anything happening. The seconds stretch on, drag out.

The terrifying thought flashes through my mind that the chute has fouled, that it has snarled around my body.

A horrible mental picture, brilliant and garish and frightening— my body spinning helplessly toward the earth, just as I have seen the dummies in the early tests tumbling, snarled in their parachutes, whirling crazily all the way down to earth.

I become frantic. Yet there remains some semblance of control, a reserve ability to *think*. I pull in my arms and run my gloved hands down my legs. As though watching from a distance, I see my hands move with amazing precision down my legs, searching for the fouled parachute. But I am only a blind man groping in his eternal darkness.

My hands find . . . nothing.

I begin to roll over in the accelerating plunge to earth. I am . . . where? . . . I am on my back. My face is up. I am falling on my back, head down.

I am unaware that, in these agonizing seconds since leaving the gondola, 16,000 feet have vanished. At 60,000 feet my body reaches its terminal velocity, plunging through the air at 423 miles per hour. The temperature of the air about me is 104 degrees below zero. But I know none of these things at this time.

Slowly, my body begins a turn to the left. Instantly, I recognize the motion; I have made many free falls, of up to sixty seconds' duration. My reaction is instinctive: immediately I drop my left arm.

The spin ends at once.

Then there is a new movement. My body begins a turn to the right. I drop my right leg, lower my right arm. Again the spinning stops even as it begins.

The thought comes to me that I can, perhaps, employ this technique all the way down into denser atmosphere. There has been only that one burst of panic. I still know fear; fear that is very much with me but not enough to prevent my thinking, trying to rationalize, doing what I can to overcome . . . whatever it is. It must be the parachute, snarled around my body, *somewhere.*

Perhaps there is the chance now that I may be able to fall semi-stabilized into the denser air, to continue to control my body movements. Yes, with care, with instant attention to what happens, I can fall safely to lower altitude. . . .

No sooner do I find comfort in this thought than a tremendous hand explodes out of nowhere and slaps my body to the left, a stunning push that I cannot believe. In this instant my body spins crazily.

Again my movements are instinctive. I shoot out my left leg and arm to stop the spin. It has no effect.

I remember everything I know of the dreaded spin; now I follow my own lessons, heed my own warnings. I pull in my arms and legs, pull into a ball, knees up, arms close. My rate of spin seems almost to explode.

Now! I fling out my arms. I am a body, jerking spasmodically, deliberately, into the spread-eagle position.

No good! The spin continues!

Now comes the deadliest sound of all, the whisper of danger rushing after me.

Swish! Swish! Swish!

Faster and faster, still accelerating, faster and faster! I sink into helplessness. I realize fully that as my body increases its speed in the spin I am hurtling into a situation that may rob me of all conscious volition to help myself.

I can feel it, a sickening sensation washing over me; invisible forces whirl my body around. Faster. . . .

I want the spinning to stop; I want nothing so desperately in my life.

I pray . . . I feel that I will die.

On my left arm is the altimeter. I want to look at the dial; I *must* look at the dial to see if I am low enough to pull the ripcord of the reserve parachute to stop the spinning. I try to pull in my left arm. . . .

I cannot move! I cannot move my arms or my legs. I am immobile, as if the centrifugal force whirling me around had jabbed me helplessly onto some enormous stakes thrust through my body and each of my limbs.

I cannot hold down the panic. It wells up, bubbling and black and red. I know what is happening; I am sick with fear; I can do nothing.

I am losing peripheral vision.

And then, praying as hard as I can, praying for my life to be spared, I see the dark curtains closing.

Blackness crashes down on me.

Again there is no time.

I open my eyes. My mind wanders. What . . . ? There has been blackness; how can I see? Am I alive?

Then, slowly, there comes the glorious wonder of the sight before my eyes. There, above me, the marvelous shape of the canopy, the red and white panels straining beautifully into the air, holding me, lowering me in the harness safely toward the earth. I want to shout with the joy and wonder of it!

I will not know for some time yet what has happened—Francis Beaupre [designer of the parachute] has saved my life. The line between the small pilot chute and the main canopy of the reserve parachute is made to withstand a pull of more than 1500 pounds. Beaupre had calculated, however, that if ever I needed the reserve parachute, I might be unconscious. He proceeded in his genius to extrapolate a situation in which I might be spinning, and the aneroid would automatically deploy the parachute. Were this to happen, he reasoned, then the pilot chute would emerge, only to entangle in the main canopy of the chute that must be snarled. The man saw all this in his mind and replaced the strong nylon with a line of only one-tenth its strength.

Because he did so, I lived. Later, I would study the film from the camera in my instrument kit. I would see the canopy of the reserve chute come out and become hopelessly entangled above me. The tremendous force of the spin would whirl the pilot chute around; but then, as Beaupre planned, the weaker nylon line would snap to free the reserve chute main canopy. It would catch the air, blossom outward and fill, eleven seconds after opening.

I know nothing of this as I drift toward the earth. I know only that I am impossibly, wonderfully alive. The sound of the recovery helicopter's blades reaches my ears.

Minutes later, I drop into the white gypsum sands of the desert, roll over on my back. I do not move.

The main parachute is wrapped around my neck.

I lie there on the sands as the men from the helicopter rush toward me. Gratitude spills in a torrent into me.

I whisper, "Thank you, God. . . ."

I cannot forget, then or later, or now, those men, the men of my team who tried to foresee every eventuality . . . and who gave me back my life.

Joe Kittinger went back to 76,000 feet for the second jump of Project Excelsior. This time, everything went perfectly, and Joe dropped out of the upper sky under perfect stability.

But Excelsior I and II were proving flights only, to test out the equipment and the procedures to be established for the greatest jump of all.

For Excelsior III, Joe Kittinger would ascend in an open gondola beneath a balloon to a height of 102,800 feet. At this height more than 99.2 per cent of the atmosphere lay beneath his feet. As he fell earthward in his spectacular leap, Joe spoke into a tape recorder.

In the comments to follow, the actual words recorded during the descent are shown in capital letters; the copy that accompanies each brief capitalized statement are remarks made by Joe Kittinger at a later date, as he listened to the tape.

Atop the planet, Joe described space as absolutely black— and fantastic. He called it a very "beautiful, beautiful world . . . a hostile sky. As you look up the sky looks beautiful but hostile."

He could see clearly for more than four hundred miles. Getting ready for the greatest jump ever attempted—then or now —he shuffled to the edge of the gondola. Only the clothes and equipment he wore on his body protected him from an explosive and violent death.

I look up, and the words ring clear and sharp as I say, "Lord, take care of me now. . . ."

I step out, 102,800 feet above the earth.

For the third time in my life I know the fantasy of being suspended in space, my body defying the law of gravity. No wind hisses in my ears or billows my clothing. There is no sound, no movement. . . .

Only for the briefest of moments. The instant I leave the balloon I start to kick my arms and legs. This time I am going to control everything that happens to me!

As I fall away from the gondola, I kick my arms and legs vigorously to begin a roll to the left. I have absolute control of my body, and my rapid leg and arm movements twist my body in the fall so that I roll around to a position on my back. It seems that I do not fall but simply twist my body position around. And then, exulting in this precise control, I leave the edge of space, falling as I wish on my back so that I may look up. . . .

There, not over a hundred feet away, looms a tremendous globe of incandescent white light. It is fully two hundred feet in diameter and glows a brilliant and rich white, the great balloon against a backdrop of the absolute black of space.

I hold my breath. There is no noise, no sound, no sensation of acceleration or falling: that same nothingness of Excelsior I. But that jump is now behind me, a matter of experience; anticipating the sensation, I am free of alarm, free to look.

The fantastic sight before my eyes is stunning to behold. I am suspended in space. Above me the brilliant globe of the balloon shoots away, explodes upward from the earth with unbelievable speed, shrinking rapidly in size. With impossibly swift acceleration, the shining globe rockets away from the earth. If I did not know that the balloon still floated serenely, I would swear that I was not moving. But of course, I am accelerating rapidly toward the earth.

I look for the stars. Dropping on my back, I am desperate to see the celestial display as no man has ever seen it, my eyes separated from space only by that thin face plate. . . . Bitter disappointment stabs at me, for I cannot see the stars. I am light-blinded. I see only the shrinking white dot of the balloon against an impenetrable velvet blackness.

I seem not to make the move consciously, but . . . I now grasp the ripcord. Perhaps it will be necessary to open the stabilization chute by manual pull, I do not know, but I am prepared to yank the D-ring.

Exactly sixteen seconds after stepping out from the gondola, I feel the trembling vibration of the timer. At once I am conscious of the minor jolt as the timer yanks the cable to release the pins of the pack strapped to my body.

There is no opening shock, nothing at all! I do not change position after the timer fires; the thought flashes to me that I must use the manual override.

There is no need to do so. Suddenly I realize I am falling with my feet to earth. There has been no opening shock whatsoever!

Captain Joseph Kittinger, USAF, falls away from his balloon gondola at an altitude of 102,800 feet! Automatic cameras took pictures of Kittinger flailing his arms and legs in successful attempt to roll over onto his back in start of longest free fall in history. (Air Force)

Only a gradual, unnoticeable change from unstabilized free fall to the attainment of our goal—I am stabilized as I plunge toward the earth.

CHUTE OPENED. . . . Sixteen seconds . . . at this instant I suck in deeply, gratefully of air. It is my first breath since stepping away from the gondola.

THIRTY SECONDS. I read off the time from the stopwatch on my wrist. From here on I study the stopwatch and altimeter almost continuously: everything that happens to me now must correlate to time and altitude. This is the key to gaining specific data and lends full meaning to my spoken words. Thus, the stopwatch and altimeter become a guide for my reports. But more important to me—for at this moment I am passing through 90,000 feet and falling with the awesome speed of 702 miles per hour—this is my total world, my only link with reality.

MULTISTAGE IS WORKING PERFECTLY! I feel the gentle tugging of Beaupre's stabilization parachute against the straps of my harness. It is the touch of an angel on my shoulder, a marvelous, exhilarating feeling. . . .

CAN'T GET MY BREATH. . . . Suddenly I feel as if I were being strangled by some invisible force! I knew this problem briefly during Excelsior II; we thought we had it whipped. But the strangling becomes worse. . . . I fight desperately for air. Gray clouds swirl through my brain; I fear I will lose consciousness.

CAN'T GET MY . . . BREATH. . . . I am gasping. The choking sensation lasts for some fifty seconds total. Then the pressure vanishes. I breathe normally, am grateful.

STABILIZED PERFECT! A ringing note of jubilation in my voice. I say to myself, *Thank you, Beau.* . . .

SEVENTY THOUSAND. One minute since leaving the gondola. . . . With each sweep of the second hand, an elation grows within me. Each second as I fall I race back into air closer to earth, air dense and rich and warm. It is a plunge back into the elixir of life. . . .

PERFECT STABILITY. As I fall, I make the most of the extraordinary stability of Beaupre's chute. I am able to start slowly to turn

Kittinger starts his body roll onto his back, as he kicks and swings his arms. Sixteen seconds after leaving the balloon gondola, Kittinger's falling speed was 702 miles per hour! (Air Force)

either to the right or to the left. These are the gentlest of motions. I use my feet as rudders. . . . As I turn to the left, I lift my left foot slightly and the roll (not a spin) stops. I start or stop motion any time I wish. The control I have is utterly fantastic! All this time, the gentle tug on my shoulders continues. As I descend I begin to feel the effects of wind from the increasing density of air; the legs of my flying suit flutter in the wind like the rippling of a flag in a stiff breeze. My earphones reduce the sound of the wind to the barest whisper. [The tape recording, however, reveals the noise of the wind as a constant and very loud howl.]

BEAUTIFUL! How perfect a jump can be! Everything is going beautifully! I am almost wild with elation!

MINUTE AND THIRTY-FIVE SECONDS. Getting closer and closer to earth. No! More important, I am rapidly leaving the hostile environment. That matters more than being closer to earth. . . . The peak of danger is now ninety-five seconds above me.

MULTISTAGE . . . BEAUTIFUL STABILITY. Everything working flawlessly. I think of the horror I knew on the first Excelsior jump. How incredibly different, how perfect this is!

MULTISTAGE PERFECT. It is simply incredible! What a magnificient experience!

SIXTY THOUSAND. Everything is going perfectly. . . .

[Two unintelligible statements.]

FIFTY THOUSAND. My body has decelerated now from its peak speed of 702 miles per hour; my speed is now 250 miles per hour. I am back, with incredible ease, at that altitude I marked on my ascent as the beginning of the area of no return. Now I know jubilation. Even if the pressure suit fails, I am within a reasonably dense atmosphere. . . . Within seconds I will no longer require body pressurization.

PERFECT STABILITY. It is a flawless descent. . . .

I'M GOING TO TURN TO THE RIGHT. I'm getting cocky now; I experiment again to see just what I can really do with this amazing parachute. I know I can stop any turning. Now I want to see just how much control I can get while making stronger, deliberate motions. I face toward the south, toward Texas. I start into a right turn; I want to look north toward Albuquerque.

The last stage of an extraordinary, record-shattering, and perfect mission: Kittinger descends toward the New Mexico desert beneath his main parachute canopy in the greatest parachute jump ever made. (Air Force)

BEAUTIFUL. I stop right on the button! I am exactly where I wish to be. What marvelous control!

PERFECT! It is simply fabulous. . . . The control is almost impossible to believe.

FACE PLATE GETTING FOGGED UP. I am passing through the coldest regions of the atmosphere; I fall through air that is 98 degrees below zero. Because of the rapid dissipation of the mask heat from windblast, thin edges of fog start to form on the sides and bottom of the face plate.

FORTY THOUSAND. . . . Coming down!

TWO MINUTES THIRTY SECONDS. It seems impossible that I have been falling this long. Everything is going so beautifully!

OUT OF POSITIVE PRESSURE. No more body constriction from the pressure suit.

THE FACE PLATE FOGGED UP A LITTLE BIT. . . .

THIRTY-FIVE THOUSAND. I check my altimeter more frequently. . . . Main canopy scheduled to go at 18,000.

LITTLE COLD IN MY LEGS.

THIRTY THOUSAND. . . . NO. . . . CORRECTION: THIRTY-FOUR.

COMING UP ON THREE MINUTES. . . . PERFECT STABILITY!

FACE PLATE'S GETTING FOGGED UP . . . TAKING OFF MY SUN VISOR . . . CAN'T GET IT LOOSE . . . HERE WE GO—IT'S OFF. MAYBE THAT WILL HELP. . . . AWFUL BRIGHT. . . .

THIRTY THOUSAND. . . .

THREE MINUTES THIRTY SECONDS.

UNDERCAST BENEATH ME. Now the clouds, so remote a short time ago, rush rapidly toward me. I have never before dropped in a free fall into clouds. I reassure myself that they are vapor and not the unyielding earth.

PERFECT STABILITY! . . . OVERRIDE IN MY HAND FOR THE PACK OPENING.

COMING UP ON TWENTY THOUSAND! . . . MULTISTAGE IS BEAUTIFUL . . . PERFECT STABILITY.

FOUR MINUTES! . . . THE UNDERCAST BENEATH ME. . . . THE MULTISTAGE IS GOING PERFECT . . . BEAUTIFUL!

FOUR MINUTES TEN SECONDS. . . . I CAN TURN AROUND PERFECT. . . . CAN DO EVERYTHING.

TWENTY THOUSAND.

FOUR MINUTES TWENTY-FIVE SECONDS. . . . FOUR MINUTES THIRTY SECONDS. WE'RE GOING INTO THE OVERCAST. . . . INTO THE OVERCAST! THE MAIN CHUTE JUST OPENED . . . RIGHT ON THE BUTTON! FOUR MINUTES AND THIRTY-SEVEN SECONDS FREE FALL. EIGHTEEN THOUSAND FEET. . . . AHHHHHHHH, BOY!

THANK YOU, GOD, THANK YOU. . . . THANK YOU FOR PROTECTING ME DURING THAT LONG DESCENT. . . . THANK YOU, GOD. . . . THANK YOU.

Epilogue

THIS, THEN, is the story of the silken angels.

But as we have seen, it is also the story of men. And whenever we speak of men like those we have met in this book, we tell a story of courage, of dedication, and of daring.

It is also a story of belief. Who is to say, after learning what we have learned, that miracles do not happen?